The Open Univer

U116

Environment: journeys through a changing world

Block 4
Life in Amazonia

Parts 1–3

Michael Gillman

This publication forms part of the Open University course U116 *Environment: journeys through a changing world*. Details of this and other Open University courses can be obtained from the Student Registration and Enquiry Service, The Open University, PO Box 197, Milton Keynes MK7 6BJ, United Kingdom (tel. +44 (0)845 300 60 90; email general-enquiries@open.ac.uk).

Alternatively, you may visit the Open University website at www.open.ac.uk where you can learn more about the wide range of courses and packs offered at all levels by The Open University.

To purchase a selection of Open University course materials visit www.ouw.co.uk, or contact Open University Worldwide, Walton Hall, Milton Keynes MK7 6AA, United Kingdom for a brochure (tel. +44 (0)1908 858793; fax +44 (0)1908 858787; email ouw-customer-services@open.ac.uk).

The Open University
Walton Hall, Milton Keynes
MK7 6AA
First published 2009.

Edited and designed by The Open University.

Typeset by SR Nova Pvt. Ltd, Bangalore, India.

Printed and bound in the United Kingdom by Halstan Printing Group, Amersham.

ISBN 978 0 7492 2089 1

1.1

Contents

Introduction to Block 4

Suddenly this was the jungle of the old books which teased my childhood, those quartos full of rich engravings showing men no more important than insects against torrential cataract and towering wood.

(The Jungle and the Damned, *Hassoldt Davis, n.d. (probably mid 1950s)*)

The hayawa tree perfumes the woods around: pairs of scarlet Aras are continually crossing the river. The maam sends forth its plaintive note, the wren chants its evening song. The caprimulgus wheels in busy flight around the canoe, while 'whip-poor-will' sits on the broken stump near the water's edge, complaining as the shades of the night set in.

(Wanderings in South America, *Charles Waterton, 1889 (original journey 1812)*)

The complete hunting outfit consists of the generally 12 to 14 foot long blow-gun (Cura of the Macusis, Ihrua of the Paravilhanos), the quiver (Muyeh), arrows (Cungwa), the lower jaw of the voracious pirate-fish (*Pygocentrus niger*), the seed covering ('silk cotton') of the *Bombax globosum* and the fibres of *Bromelia karatas*. But of the whole apparatus the Macusis only finish the latter parts: they obtain the blowgun in barter from the Arecunas, Maiongkong and Guianaus.

(Travels in British Guiana, *Richard Schomburgk, 1840*)

The sloth, about the size of a large sheepdog, hung upside down and stared at me with an expression of ineffable sadness on its furry face. Slowly it opened its mouth, exposing its black enamel-less teeth, and did its best to frighten me by making the loudest noise of which it is capable – a faint bronchial wheeze.

(Zoo Quest to Guiana, *David Attenborough, 1956, 'Famous T.V. Producer brings them back Alive'*)

These quotations illustrate both the complexity and the biological richness of the tropical forest of South America, and the fascination and awe it has inspired in European travellers.

This block will take you on a journey through Amazonia (Figure I.1(a)) that I hope will similarly inspire you. Part 1 will introduce you to its biological richness, splendour and spectacle and will demonstrate the importance of it both to indigenous peoples, who have lived there for thousands of years, and to the world beyond. Part 2 will look at the Amazon basin as a whole system to show its importance to the world's climate by explaining its role in the global carbon cycle. The use of forest products both commercially and by local people is explored through the concept of ecological sustainability. The focus of Part 3 is on the regional and global interactions that will affect the future of Amazonia and its peoples.

Figure I.1 The location of Amazonia and a selection of (iconic) images: (a) map of the Amazonia region; (b) a three-toed sloth (*Bradypus* sp.); (c) forest loss/fragmentation; (d) Amazonian people in traditional dress. (sp. means a species of that genus.)

Many of the plants and animals of Amazonia are endemic (for example the sloth in Figure I.1(b)), that is, they are found nowhere else on Earth, and they provide a wide range of medicinal and food products for humans. The value to humans is further enhanced by the pivotal role of the Amazonian forest in climate change, with the potential to influence greatly the levels of greenhouse gases such as carbon dioxide. Yet despite the importance of the forest of Amazonia to people across the world it is being rapidly lost (Figure I.1(c)).

You may have noticed that none of the above quotes are from the indigenous peoples of the region (Figure I.1(d)); this is because their tradition has been to communicate orally rather than by writing. Perceptions of the forest have been perpetuated by travellers who generally returned to European comfort and were often aided by large teams of local people. However, Europeans have also documented much of the local knowledge of the forest, some of which had been lost to indigenous peoples as their lifestyles changed. These records illustrate how local names for different trees and forest products demonstrated a remarkable understanding of the richness of the forest long before 'scientific' terminology. Some of the activities in this block will redress the balance of European perspectives by seeking the views of indigenous peoples of their environment.

Disturbance and loss of tropical forest has been one of the great subjects of global concern, especially since the 1970s. The recognition that tropical forest is home to an enormous number of different types of plant and animal has generated a series of local, regional and global conservation initiatives. On your journey through the forest and other Amazonian environments you will be able to pause to reflect on the success or otherwise of these initiatives. Sustainable solutions require local participation and support. In this block you will see how indigenous people view and use the forest and other environments.

Part 1
Ecosystems and Amazonia

Michael Gillman

Introduction

1

This first part of the block treats Amazonia as broadly the tropical region of South America (Figure I.1(a)). For the purposes of this text, the Amazon basin is the same geographical area as Amazonia, but the term 'Amazon basin' refers specifically to the catchment of the Amazon river. Some fundamental ecological concepts will be explained and will be explored with examples from Amazonia. The concepts enable environments to be interpreted and categorised, and their processes of change to be better understood. You will journey into different parts of Amazonia and encounter a wide range of inhabitants. You will meet one of the indigenous groups, the Arawak people of Wakapoa in Guyana, and spend a little time with them. You will learn about how their livelihoods are supported by their knowledge of their environment.

Knowledge is a key theme of this part. I will look at how scientific knowledge is created and applied to Amazonia and in the process will build your understanding of scientific terminology. I will look at the knowledge held by the indigenous peoples of Amazonia and how their knowledge, like that of the Inuit peoples of the Arctic, is focused on helping them obtain a livelihood from the forest and other environments.

2   Ecosystems defined

Our journey into Amazonia reveals a wide range of different environments, of which the classic 'jungle' is one. The word 'jungle' will not be used here as its meaning is too vague. Instead it is helpful to introduce some new words which will aid understanding of the complexity of the connections of life in Amazonia (Box 1.1 gives an example of interactions between species).

The term 'environment' refers to the surroundings of a particular organism. Generally, when the word environment is used it refers to our environment, i.e. the environment as experienced or perceived by humans. Because scientists often study non-human environments and need to be more precise about the meaning of environment (and because they like to generate a rich additional vocabulary!), a set of words has been generated to identify more clearly the different attributes of environments.

Habitat. The word habitat (defined in Block 1) is used to indicate the area where an organism lives. The habitats of the jaguar are tropical forest and (less often) savannah grassland, where a single jaguar will occupy a home range. Within those habitats there will be many occupants alongside the jaguar.

Community. A combination of plants, animals and other organisms interacting together is described as a community or, more accurately, a *biological community*.

Box 1.1   An example of interaction: food

Examples of interactions between individuals of different species include feeding interactions, where the different species form part of a food chain or web. Food chains and food webs indicate the feeding relationships between different species. A food chain shows a simple linear series of feeding relationships; for example

Forest tree leaves (producer) → sloth (herbivore) → harpy eagle (carnivore).

Such simple food chains are in fact rare. Herbivores generally feed on a range of different green plants and herbivores are preyed on by a range of different carnivores, which in turn prey on a range of herbivores. Complex feeding relationships between organisms are known as food webs; a food web is essentially a map of many simple, connected food chains.

Food webs and energy

In the process of photosynthesis that occurs in all green plants, a simple sugar – glucose – is formed. Carbon dioxide from the atmosphere and water from the soil are the raw materials, and chlorophyll (which makes plants green) enables the process to occur using the light energy from the sun. Plants use this sugar, together with substances from the soil such as nitrates, phosphates, sulphates and potassium, to manufacture many other kinds of complex, organic molecules that make up the tissues of the growing plant. Living organisms such as green plants that carry out this process are known as producers.

Herbivores, or primary consumers, are animals that eat plants and in turn use the plant materials they absorb to sustain their own growth. Secondary consumers, or carnivores, in turn eat these animals, and so on. These kinds of feeding relationships are summarised in Figure 1.1 as a food chain. A food chain is a hierarchy of plants and animals based on who eats whom. Each level or link in the food chain is called a trophic level. The producers are the first level, primary consumers the second level, and so on.

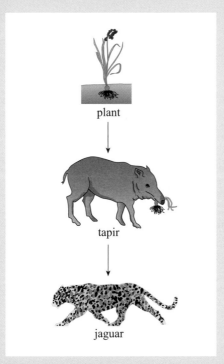

Figure 1.1 Example of a food chain in a tropical rainforest

In practice, the feeding relationships of animals and plants in ecosystems are not as simple as Figure 1.1 might suggest. The jaguar may feed on other mammals, and the plant may be eaten by a variety of primary consumers. The multiple feeding relationships that exist between plant and animal species are more accurately described as food webs (an example is given in Figure 1.2).

If you look carefully at Figure 1.2 you will see that there is another level below primary producers. This is the detritus level. The dead remains of plants and animals form the food for many different animals, fungi and bacteria. These detritivores (detritus feeders) break down plant and animal tissue back into simple substances such as CO_2 and nitrates which can then be used by producers.

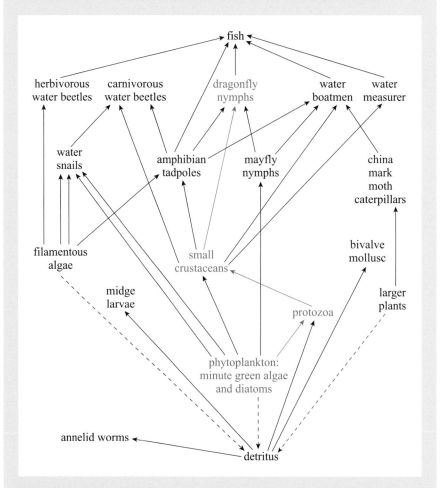

Figure 1.2 Pond ecosystem (not a tropical example, but many of the component species groups will be found in tropical and temperate regions)

Complex organic molecules move from plant to primary consumer to secondary or tertiary consumer. The common chemical constituent of these complex molecules is carbon, so food webs are a way in which carbon can move through and around ecosystems.

When plants manufacture glucose (a carbohydrate) in photosynthesis they are producing the compound from which whole food webs can be sustained. In addition, within each molecule of glucose, energy from sunlight is fixed as chemical energy within the chemical bonds of the molecule. So not only does matter move through food chains but so does energy.

Energy is needed to make new plant tissue from the glucose that is produced during photosynthesis, and this energy comes from the breakdown of glucose molecules, which liberates the energy within the chemical bonds. In this process of respiration (look back at Section 3.3 of Block 1 if you need reminding), one of the waste products is carbon dioxide, which is liberated back to the atmosphere. Similarly, when a primary consumer eats a plant, some of the compounds that are absorbed into the animal will be broken down, in respiration, to power the functions of the animal – movement, chemical reactions and so on, and carbon dioxide will be released.

Niche. The *ecological niche* is a term used to describe the place and role of a species in a community. The ecological niche of a species describes more than the precise place where it lives; it also includes what it does there, i.e. its behaviour, mode of feeding and role in the community. Different species may occupy the same ecological niche in different communities. For example, vultures occupy the ecological niche of large mobile species feeding on large dead animals in forests and savannahs, which in Britain is filled by crows and magpies.

Ecosystem. If all the non-living elements of a community (dead wood, non-living parts of the soil, the air in that area) and the interactions between them are included within the community, the term ecosystem is used. Thus ecosystem is the highest level of description of all the components within a given area. Study of ecosystems includes consideration of the way in which elements such as carbon move between different parts of the whole. An ecosystem might link together several different habitats. A bird that feeds on a fruit in a tropical forest and drops it or defecates in a grassland area on its way to another piece of forest is providing a biological link between the two habitats.

The term biome was introduced in Block 2. This is generally used to refer to large areas of the planet that have climatic and environmental conditions that determine the ecosystems and habitats to be found there, for example tundra or desert. As with many of the terms discussed here, different systems of classification are in use and a detailed discussion of these is not necessary.

There may be other interactions, such as competition for space or light. For example, two tree seedlings growing in the same small gap in the forest may compete for light. Figure 1.3 shows some examples.

The outcomes of interactions between species are not always obvious. When a harpy eagle plucks a sloth from the tree canopy there is just one winner. However, when a bat takes nectar from a flower it is not only helping itself to a sugar-rich meal, but also benefiting the plant by spreading its pollen to other members of the same species, thereby ensuring a mixing of genetic information. Similarly, a plant may benefit by having its fruit eaten by monkeys because the seed will be dispersed to a new location, either by passing through the digestive system of the monkey or by being dropped after the monkey has removed the fruit. Some seeds will only germinate after passing through a digestive system. Other feeding interactions are not always what they seem. Leaf-cutter ants do not actually eat the leaves they cut. Instead, they remove them to an underground area where they grow a fungus on them and they then eat the fungus.

(a)

(b)

(c)

Figure 1.3 Interactions in Amazonian habitats: (a) monkey feeding on fruit; (b) harpy eagle, a top predator; (c) leaf-cutter ants

To summarise, there are three important words that help to describe particular sections of the environment and its inhabitants: *habitat* (place where an organism lives), *biological community* (the group of organisms in one or more habitats) and *ecosystem* (the community and associated non-living components in one or more habitats). The importance of the term ecosystem will become clearer shortly, but for now you should recognise the two key parts of the word: *eco-* (Block 1 explained the various uses of *eco*, from the Greek word for home, *oikos*) and *system*, discussed in Block 3. Ecological comes from *ecology*, which is the study (*logos*) of the interactions of organisms with their biological and non-biological environment, for example the way organisms feed or compete amongst themselves.

2.1   Boundaries

The above example of a bird creating a connection between two habitats reveals a problem with the concept of ecosystems. Where does one ecosystem start and another one end?

There is no easy answer to this question. Indeed, it could be argued that the question itself is flawed because any given ecosystem, like any of the other terms described, or other systems, is whatever a particular observer delineates it to be, so it is artificial. Certainly, placing a boundary on an ecosystem, habitat or community is a difficult and essentially subjective exercise. It is therefore a good idea to be clear about the definition and boundaries that have been used when considering ecological information in any detail.

So, can a tropical forest be considered as a single habitat? Not really, because different species live in different parts of it. So, there are soil-living organisms, hence the soil can be regarded as one habitat, and canopy-living organisms, hence the canopy is a second habitat.

Study note: more on note taking

To help you make notes on this discussion of ecological concepts, three techniques are presented in Figure 1.4. These are a simple list, a simple line diagram and a more complex diagram. Using the example of a food chain that is part of a food web you can see that, depending on the content, one technique may be more appropriate than another. So a simple list would be sufficient to describe the relatively simple, one-way interactions in a food chain, but a picture diagram is a much better tool for visualising the complexities of the food web of which that chain is a part.

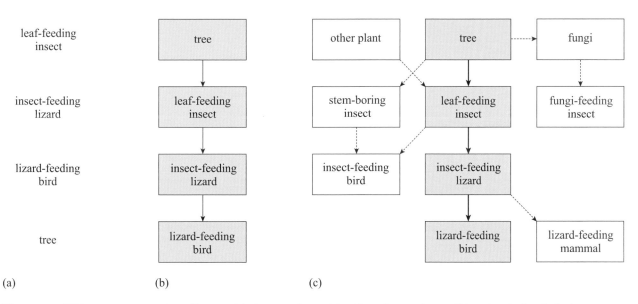

Figure 1.4 Different ways to describe trophic interactions: (a) a list of organisms; (b) a simple food chain; (b) a food web

Activity 1.1   Note-taking techniques

1   In the three examples shown in Study note: *more on note taking* above the information is presented in different ways. Can you describe the different stories that are being told in each of the three examples?

2   Which of these noting devices did you use? Why did you choose this device over the other two?

Discussion

1   The first example was a set of key words, which does not show the relationships between the terms used.

   The second example illustrates the linear relationship between trophic levels, showing what eats what, i.e. a food chain.

   The third example shows the food chain in the context of links with other organisms, i.e. a food web. It is visually appealing and perhaps easier to remember. However, such a picture can soon get cluttered and some terms could not be fitted in.

2   In explaining your choice, you may have said that you made notes the way you always do, or the quickest way if time was short. I hope that the study note and the activity will encourage you to try a range of devices and find which works best for you as an aid to memory.

This detailed discussion of key concepts and an activity around them has been provided as they are some of the tools needed for making sense of the relationships that make up the forest. As in all subjects, categorisation aids communication, in this case allowing consistent identification of types of environment.

The latter is important because different types of ecosystem function in different ways or at different rates. Scientists who study terrestrial (land) ecosystems often categorise them according to the dominant types of plant. Dominance in this sense refers to the most common (or abundant) plant in an area. Thus, woodland and forest is dominated by trees, grassland is dominated by grasses, and scrub has a bit of each. These environments also vary in other ways, for example in terms of the amount of water in the soil, leading to categories such as wet woodland or dry grassland.

Summary of Section 2

Now that you have an understanding of the important basic terminology and concepts, the next section will use this in a discussion of four ecosystems that cover most of the lowland regions of Amazonia. They are the savannah grassland, aquatic, mangrove and tropical forest ecosystems. Notice at this stage that the emphasis is on general features of the ecosystems rather than on a more detailed analysis. Where it is useful in helping you to envisage the type of ecosystem under discussion I have provided examples from elsewhere around the globe and discussed their status.

Ecosystems in Amazonia

3

3.1   Savannah grassland

Because the Amazonian forest is so well known it is easy to forget that there is any other type of ecosystem in the region. Whilst the grasslands of central and southern Africa are familiar through their charismatic carnivores and herbivores (lions, cheetahs, elephants and so on) there are some equally impressive areas of grassland in South America, albeit with a rather more modest set of inhabitants. These grasslands, like their African cousins, are collectively referred to as savannah (Figure 1.5), which indicates that there is a scattering of trees. In savannah the density of trees is not sufficient to stop the growth of grass and there is a wide spectrum from true forest through savannah to open grassland, categorised according to the amount of tree cover.

Figure 1.5 Savannah with termite mound and anteater

Some of the animal inhabitants of the savannah are extraordinary. These include that most unusual of creatures, the giant anteater (Figure 1.5), which may be up to two metres in length from head to tail and weigh up to 40 kilograms. In order to support such a large body the giant anteater must consume a vast number of ants and similar creatures such as termites on a daily basis. The termites present an obvious target as their enormous mounds punctuate the landscape. Giant anteaters use their large front claws to rip open the mounds and then lick up the termites with their long, sticky tongues. It has been estimated that giant anteaters consume about 30 000 termites per day!

These grasslands may vary dramatically between the wet and dry seasons. In the wet season they may be extensively flooded, whilst in the dry season they may burn. These environmental extremes place major stresses on human and non-human inhabitants. I recall walking through the Rupununi savannah (Figure 1.6) in the late 1990s during an unusually hot and extended dry season. At that time much of the savannah was burning and threatening a wide range of communities living in the savannah and on the forest edge. The water levels were the lowest that people could remember. There is little shade in such areas: few species of tree can tolerate the extremes of condition. One tree that is widespread has the scientific name *Curatella americana*. This has the common name of toilet paper tree, so called because it is the only tree with leaves of sufficient size to serve that function and one of the few trees growing in the savannah. However, it is also a joke as the leaves are extremely dry and rough and the last thing one would choose as toilet paper.

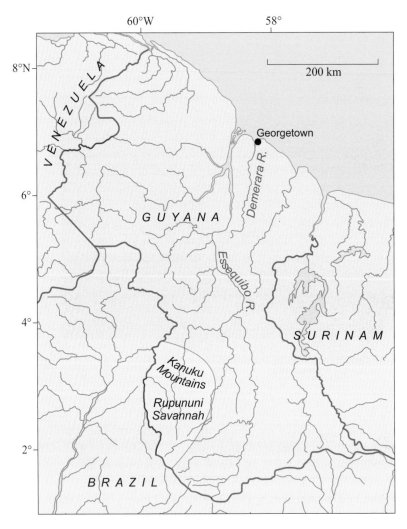

Figure 1.6 Map showing location of the Rupununi savannah

3.2   Aquatic ecosystems

Aquatic ecosystems are found in, and include, ponds, rivers and other habitats where the dominant feature is the presence of open water. So a garden pond might be one example, or we could consider the whole length of the Amazon as a single aquatic ecosystem.

Amazonia is intersected by a large number of rivers, which join together to form the Amazon river and flow out into the Atlantic Ocean. These rivers start in the Andes, and collect to form major tributaries such as the Rio Negro, Madeira and Tapajos. You will see later how the area of Amazonia is defined by the catchments of the Amazon and its tributaries. To the north of these rivers is the Orinoco, which runs through Brazil, and the smaller Essequibo, which runs through Guyana (Figure 1.7). To the south is the Rio de la Plata, which enters the Atlantic Ocean between Uruguay and

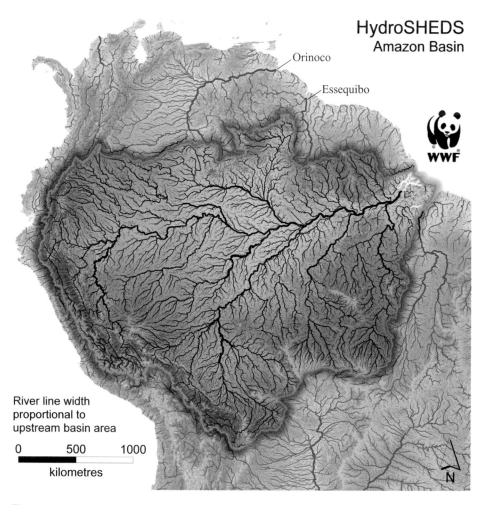

Figure 1.7 Map of Amazon river system and its relationship to the Orinoco and Essequibo

Argentina. The rivers and their tributaries are an important component of a wide range of aquatic ecosystems, which include lakes and seasonally flooded areas. Such a rich lattice of rivers and lakes indicates that much of Amazonia is a very wet place. The importance of this will be discussed when we consider the role of Amazonia in global climate control.

There are four species of river dolphin in the world, and collectively they form one of the most endangered groups of animals. Of these, three are restricted to fresh water – living in the Amazon, the Ganges and Indus, and the Yangtze. The Yangtze river dolphin was probably extinct by 2006 (despite being a protected species since 1975). The Amazon river dolphin (Figure 1.8) occurs in both the Amazon and Orinoco basins and still occurs in reasonable numbers, although it is adversely affected by hunting, pollution and dam construction.

(a)   (b)

(c)

Figure 1.8 Amazon river species: (a) river dolphin; (b) arapaima; (c) piranha

The arapaima is the largest freshwater fish in South America, reaching lengths of 2.5 m and up to 200 kg in weight. It is a highly prized fish for human consumption and some attempts have been made to farm it. It has some interesting adaptations including an ability to take in air by its mouth, which is useful in shallow river systems with low levels of dissolved oxygen. It also rears its young in its mouth, a phenomenon known as mouthbrooding, which is found across a range of species of fish and a few frogs (Figure 1.9).

Figure 1.9 Mouthbrooding

There are several types of river-dwelling animal in Amazonia that have considerable notoriety. These include the piranha, a mainstay of Hollywood, but in fact more of a nuisance than a collective monster. It does have extremely sharp teeth, but these are helpful to local people in preparing simple tools, whilst its flesh is reasonably good for eating. Freshwater stingrays that inhabit shallow areas of rivers where people wash are more of a concern. Caiman (a type of crocodile) occur in many smaller rivers but these seldom cause injuries, although the rare black caiman can reach very large sizes and move quickly. Most feared of all is a very small, parasitic fish, the candiru, which detects animals or animal products such as urea (in urine) and swims towards the signal in search of a blood meal. Upon entering the unfortunate animal it seeks out a major artery, where it feeds. Attacks on humans are known, so urinating in the waters of the Amazon and Orinoco, where these fish live, is inadvisable!

3.3 Mangrove swamps

Mangroves refer to both the dominant trees that line the coasts and river estuaries around the tropics and the forest type within which the dominant trees exist.

The main characteristic of mangrove trees is that the roots are in salt or brackish (partly salty) water; hence they are part of an aquatic ecosystem. They are visually spectacular trees because they emerge from the water and expose a tangled network of twisting branches and roots when tides drop. In tropical regions mangroves form the interface between the terrestrial environment, such as forest, and the marine ocean environment.

Mangroves are found throughout the tropics (Figure 1.10) and any one mangrove area is dominated by a few species of mangrove tree. For example, on the Brazilian coast, where about 15% of the world's mangrove forest is to be found, there are seven species of mangrove tree belonging to four different groupings of species, namely the genera red mangrove (*Rhizophora*), black mangrove (*Avicennia*), white mangrove (*Laguncularia*) and buttonwood (*Conocarpus*). Overall, the species richness is low but some areas, such as the Maranhão region, include large numbers of shorebirds such as herons.

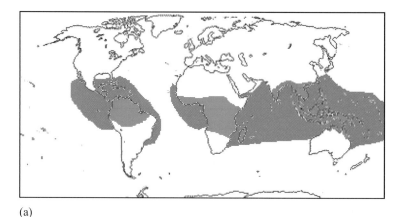

(a)

(b)

Figure 1.10 Mangroves: (a) distribution in the tropics; (b) a mangrove species

Mangrove swamps are one of the most important forest types for humans, yet also one of the most abused. Many fish that are caught commercially depend on mangrove forests for food and shelter. For example, shrimp fishing is especially important in the Maranhão region.

In addition to food production, mangroves have an important role in preventing coastal erosion as well as providing habitats for a wide range of species. However, clearance has occurred to allow waterside development and to provide fuel wood. Globally, mangrove area has declined, from 19.8 million hectares in 1980 to less than 15 million hectares by the end of 2000.

The adaptations of mangrove trees are fascinating and include mechanisms for dealing with salty water and reproduction in a coastal aquatic habitat. (You might like to try and think if there are any other trees that flourish in such an environment; there are certainly no obvious examples in Europe). Specialised root systems provide extra anchorage whilst other lateral roots grow upwards out of the water and help the plant to absorb oxygen (Figure 1.11). Excess salt is either prevented from entering the plant, secreted from the plant by salt glands or stored as crystals in the leaves. A certain amount of the accumulated salt is lost when the leaves drop. In some species seed germination may begin on the plant, with subsequent dispersal by flotation.

Figure 1.11 Newly colonising mangrove plant

Realisation of the importance of mangrove ecosystems has prompted restoration programmes and an assessment of their ecological and economic value around the world. A study in the Philippines demonstrated revenue from fisheries, tourism and timber of US$315 per hectare per year (Walton et al., 2006). This estimate excluded indirect benefits such as reduction in coastal erosion. The overwhelming perception of local fishermen was that the mangrove protected them and the fisheries from storms and typhoons. This role has been acknowledged more widely following the Indonesian tsunami of 26 December 2004, which killed more than 225 000 people (Barbier, 2006).

3.4 Tropical forest ecosystems

Whatever your level of prior knowledge, it is likely that you are familiar with the idea of tropical forests as areas with a high richness of plants and animals. Although the focus of attention here is on Amazonia, many of the principles apply to the other areas of tropical forest in the world, such as in the Congo basin in central Africa and Borneo in South-East Asia.

Tropical forests are, in fact, a diverse bunch. There are wet and dry types, lowland, montane (mountain) and *cloud forests*. In a typical lowland undisturbed forest you will find large trees, which may have a diameter of a metre or more (Figure 1.12), interspersed with smaller trees. The larger trees may extend 40 m up to the leafy canopy (the upper part of the forest

Figure 1.12 Example of tropical forest; a large, buttressed tree and other plants

where the tallest trees may form a continuous layer of leaves and branches) where monkeys and birds feed, insects pollinate and where various epiphytic plants sit or hang. The main biological activity in the forest occurs in the canopy amongst the tree leaves and at the base of the trees in the soils.

The interaction of the forest with the river systems is very important for understanding the productivity and functioning of the forest. The upland forests of tall trees that most people associate with Amazonia are examples of *terra firme* (from the Portuguese phrase for solid land), forests that do not flood. During the rainy season the Amazon and its major tributaries flood the lands adjacent to them, depositing rich silt and giving rise to highly productive floodplains.

The biodiversity of the forest is illustrated by the different types of tree. Imagine an area $100\ \text{m} \times 100\ \text{m}$ (one hectare). If you were to walk through a woodland of this size in England you might find 10 different types of tree. A similar activity in a tropical forest will return more than 100 types of tree. Indeed, in parts of Amazonia it is possible to find more than 250 different species of tree with a minimum size of 10 cm diameter (the diameter is measured at a fixed height of 1.2 m above the ground). This is many more tree species than you would find across the whole of Europe! A great deal of effort has gone into forest inventories, where the numbers of individuals of different plant species (especially trees) have been recorded in fixed areas. This information is not only important as an assessment of the great variety in tropical forests, but also as a measure of the total amount of plant material in a given area. The value of the latter will become apparent in later sections.

Summary of Section 3

This section has looked at some of the ecosystems found in Amazonia and provided a richer and more detailed understanding of the region. It has shown how different ecosystems are characterised by different sets of species.

4   Changes and cycles

In this section we will explore change more systematically. I will use the ideas of cycles and succession to help explain change. You have come across the role of cycles when you studied the carbon cycle in Block 1 and the water cycle in Block 3, Part 1. Here we begin by considering change at a smaller scale, and this is considered in detail in Part 2.

4.1   Life cycle of a tree

Tropical forests are, in ecological terms, relatively dynamic places. They do not simply sit there housing a diverse collection of exquisitely shaped structures. Consider the *life cycle* of a large tree for example (Figure 1.13), one of the fundamental biological units of any forest.

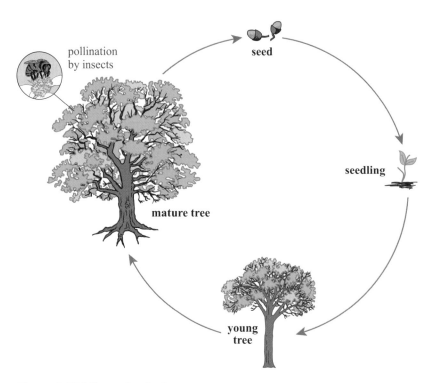

Figure 1.13 Life cycle of a tree

It begins its life as a seed. The seed arrives at the forest floor by a variety of mechanisms. It may be ejected explosively from a seed pod, it may float on a parachute of fine hairs or it may pass through the digestive system of a bird, mammal or reptile. Upon arrival on the forest floor the seed needs to be lucky. If it is not eaten or subject to disease *and* it manages to get buried at the right depth *and* it receives the correct amount of light and water, then it may germinate. Germination is the process whereby seeds begin growing, producing a root and shoot. Various conditions, such as a period of cold followed by warmth and/or the onset of rains, may be required to initiate germination. An individual tree may produce thousands of seeds each year. Only a few of those seeds may germinate. Ultimately a single large tree in an area of forest will fall and be replaced by an individual of the same species over a period of perhaps 50 years.

After germination the seedling grows, at first using some of the stored energy in the seed, but soon deriving its own energy from the sunlight falling on its leaves through the process of photosynthesis. Some seedlings will need to grow in a gap in the forest, therefore they need a tree to die and create a hole in the tree canopy. Other seedlings will grow in the shade of the canopy. Eventually the tree will reach maturity, either below the canopy or emerging into the light above the canopy; at this point the tree can start producing flowers. Most plant species require a transfer of pollen from the male to the female reproductive parts (pollination) for seeds to be formed. Some plant species are wind pollinated, whereas in others the pollen is transferred by animals such as bees, bats or hummingbirds (one plant species usually has only one method of pollination; see Figure 1.13). If pollination is successful the plant can produce seeds and the life cycle is continued.

When a tree dies and some or all of it falls, as a result of old age, disease or damage (e.g. from a lightning strike or branches breaking under their own weight), it creates a space in the canopy and disturbs the ground. So a large part of natural forest disturbance is a consequence of the life cycle of the trees. Larger-scale natural events, such as flooding, may affect much wider areas, causing the deaths of large numbers of trees. Whilst natural disturbance at different scales is a feature of the forest, many species are adapted to the (often) seasonal nature of these events. As you will see, the effects of humans need to be compared against the backdrop of natural disturbance.

Throughout its life cycle the tree supports a great number of other species – these include pollinators, fruit feeders, leaf feeders and organisms that feed on dead and decaying wood. These species will also be eaten by other species, thereby maintaining the complex food web of the forest. More information on the inhabitants of the forest will be provided in Section 6.

4.2 Structure and processes in ecosystems

Ecosystems may be defined to include a few species or many thousands of species. Similarly, they may involve a small area such as a pond or be spread across hundreds of square kilometres such as a savannah. The connections between species in the ecosystem determine how they function. One of the main functions is the movement of nutrient elements through the ecosystem. These nutrients, such as nitrogen or phosphorus, pass from plant to animal to animal through food webs and may end up in the soil or atmosphere for long periods of time. You will learn more about food webs in Part 2, but for now it is sufficient to know that various atoms and molecules are cycled within and between ecosystems. Similarly, energy will move *through* the system (and be lost at various points), starting with the Sun and ending with top carnivores, the meat eaters not eaten by anything else, for example jaguars and alligators. The point to emphasise is that ecosystems are dynamic and that change is a natural part of these systems. Thus, a tree grows and dies over time, opening up gaps in the forest for future colonisation.

It is common to think of ecosystems as self-sustaining, in that they capture energy and cycle nutrients and may persist for hundreds or thousands of years. This apparently harmonious situation breaks down for a number of reasons. There may be catastrophic disturbances, such as intense hurricanes, floods or fires, which cause a widespread loss of key species from the ecosystem (Figure 1.14). In fact, the species in many ecosystems can often recover from such disturbances – the defined ecosystem is said to be **resilient** to such change. For example, certain tree species are adapted to conditions of occasional fires (perhaps every 100 years on average) and may recover numbers through increased germination of seed and growth in the fire-cleared areas, returning these to something like the previous state. However, the system can be pushed too far and be unable to recover. A hurricane once every thirty years may allow species to recover, but if they occur more frequently then species may be driven to extinction in that area. If the species occur nowhere else then they become globally extinct, changing the nature of that ecosystem. The disturbance may not be physical, such as wind or fire, but biological – the introduction or arrival of a new species may alter the balance of other species in the ecosystem, perhaps initiating the end of that ecosystem. There is, of course, one species

Figure 1.14 Ecosystem disturbances – a savannah fire

with the ability to alter all ecosystems at unprecedented scales and rates, either through premeditated action or as an accidental consequence of other activities. The activity of this species has been felt across Amazonia as it hunts, clears, farms, mines and pollutes. Whilst some of this change may be seen in a positive light, much of this activity is either irreversible or requires very long time periods of recovery. This species is *Homo sapiens*.

4.3   Succession: the development of ecosystems

The preceding subsection hinted at ways in which ecosystems may change over time. Change may be at the scale of an individual tree, across tens or hundreds of square kilometres as a result of flooding, or thousands of square kilometres in response to climate change. In this subsection the important underlying process of succession will be discussed. Succession is the gradual process of change and development that occurs in all ecosystems over time. It is often most easily seen in terms of vegetation change, but the processes involve all the organisms present. It reveals the intrinsically dynamic nature of ecosystems and the species that live there. There are two types of succession that are recognised: primary and secondary.

4.3.1   Primary succession

Primary succession refers to the change in plants and animals over time after the creation of a new *substrate*, the surface on which an ecosystem can develop, or the complete removal of the previous one including all the plants and animals, the soil and the seeds and other living components of the soil, leaving a more or less inert substrate. Processes that can generate entirely new substrates or remove the entire former community include volcanic activity, which presents a new substrate through lava flow and may also bury previous substrates, glacial melt and other extreme events. The process of succession and some of the plants typical of different successional stages are summarised in Figure 1.15.

In the context of Amazonia the importance of primary succession is evident along the Andes mountain range, which runs like a spine down the western side of South America. The movement of the Andes over geological time has provided new substrates and altered the course and flow of the Amazon and its tributaries. Plant species that colonise volcanic and other bare rock substrates need various adaptations to help them survive. These include the ability to get there in the first place (either through wind dispersal or via a visiting bird) and then survive the conditions, which will often include a very limited supply of plant nutrients. One particularly successful group of plants is the family *Ericaceae*, which includes the familiar heathers, rhododendrons and azaleas. This family may be found on

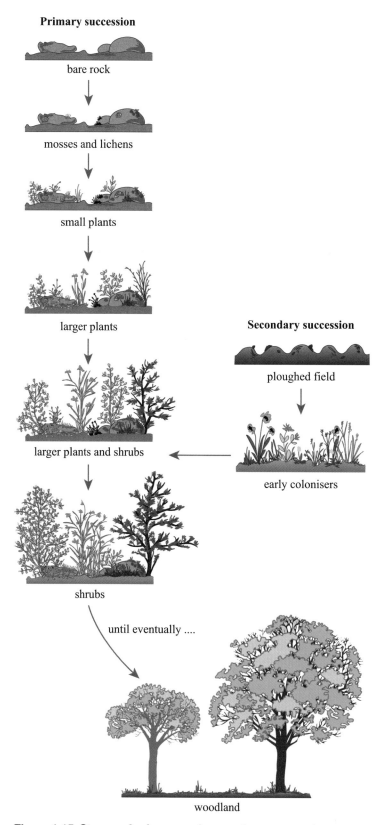

Figure 1.15 Stages of primary and secondary succession

bare rock, often at higher altitudes, in the Andes, Central America, the mountains of the Rift Valley (e.g. Mount Kenya), the Himalayas, and in the uplands of Madagascar and New Guinea. They are also found in lowland heathlands in western Europe (a heathland is an environment dominated by low-growing Ericaceae). In many of these places they show a tolerance of acidic conditions which are inherently short of available plant nutrients. Whilst the adaptations of the Ericaceae include some visible structures, such as particular types of leathery leaf, it is below ground (or between rocks; see Figure 1.16) where the most important adaptation occurs. Here the roots are assisted by a type of fungus called a *mycorrhiza* or mycorrhizal fungus. Many species of plant have mycorrhizal associations which have been shown to help plants take up essential nutrients from the soil. In return the fungus receives some of the carbon that the plant has fixed through photosynthesis. The mycorrhizae of the Ericaceae are different from those associated with other plants in both their structure and function. Whilst they fulfil some of the functions of other mycorrhizae they are also able to help the plant deal with some of the potentially toxic components of its environment, for example by storing heavy metals that are found near volcanoes.

Figure 1.16 *Pernettya (Gaultheria) prostrata* **growing in bare rock. This species is found throughout the Andes**

4.3.2   Secondary succession

Secondary succession is the colonisation of previously cleared vegetation where the soil is still in place. This is the type of succession familiar to most people, in which an area of land is cleared and is re-colonised by fast-growing species, which are often short lived, followed by shrub species and tree species (Figure 1.15). Each of these sets of species are referred to as successional stages. The process of re-colonisation can depend on the seeds in the soil and on seeds blown in from nearby plants or dropped by animals from neighbouring areas. Like primary succession, secondary succession often follows a well-ordered route. Indeed, as soil builds in a primary succession it may become indistinguishable from secondary succession, with the same plants (or types of plant) occupying different stages (Figure 1.15). The rate of primary or secondary succession can be measured as the time taken by species characteristic of different successional stages to colonise an area. The rate of secondary succession can depend on many factors. For example, small trees may act as perches for birds, which defecate seeds of later successional species, which speeds up the process of succession. The final stage of succession is known as the *climax community*. This is an apparently stable state, whose appearance and general makeup may remain constant over many years, although the individual organisms making up that community will change.

Activity 1.2   Ecosystem changes over time

We can regard a garden or urban park as a managed ecosystem.

1 Describe the basic cyclic and non-cyclic processes that occur in such an ecosystem.

2 To what extent does succession occur in the system?

Discussion

1 As with any ecosystem, the key non-cyclic process is the flow of energy through it, from sunlight trapped by the plants into their tissues, the consumption of these tissues by a variety of species including birds, snails and humans, and the release of this energy back to the surroundings, mainly through respiration of all organisms. Carbon will also cycle through the system rather than accumulating in the soil in most parks or gardens, where dead plant material is carefully removed. Some of the carbon that is respired by plants and soil organisms may be reabsorbed by the plants, but most of it probably just flows through the system. Other elements that are plant nutrients are often added to the system by human managers in the form of fertilisers. Some of these nutrients may be recycled through the return of vegetable matter that has been dug back into the soil, or removed and composted before returning to the system. Some of these nutrients will be lost into water percolating down through the soil or running across the surface, but human management is usually designed to try and minimise such effects by careful choice of sown species and management of residues.

2 In most gardens and parks, the processes of succession are repeatedly stopped by human intervention, but on a freshly cleared plot, the invasive plants that grow represent the first stage of a secondary succession. In parkland that has wooded areas, the successional processes outlined for the Amazon forests would occur, although for safety reasons, tree fall is usually pre-empted by tree surgery. However, where gaps are opened and left for any reason, some secondary succession is always likely to occur.

Summary of Section 4

This section has explored change by considering the contribution that the life cycle of a tree makes to forest environments, in terms of both the life it supports and the life it gives way for. It then discussed other, large cycles that occur within ecosystems and how these combine to cause succession, the life cycle of an ecosystem. Through understanding how change occurs it is easier to appreciate some of the processes that affect biodiversity in Amazonia, to which we now turn.

5   Biodiversity: understanding species richness

In Section 3 you were introduced to a small number of the inhabitants of Amazonia in relation to the main ecosystems. Before launching into a description of the extraordinary array of life in the natural environments of Amazonia, it is necessary to step back and consider more carefully how to describe and so record this great variety. These concepts are readily transferable as they can be used to describe any ecosystem and its components.

5.1   Taxonomy: the classification of organisms

The reason for classifying different living organisms is primarily so that some kind of order can be created as a way of describing the millions of species that exist in the world. It also provides a useful and quick means of identification and communication.

However, there is more to taxonomy than just putting organisms that share characteristics into groups for convenience. A modern classification aims to show the evolutionary relationships between different groups of living organisms. By using modern methods of determining genetic information to show relationships between species, a phylogenetic evolutionary tree of life or *phylogeny* can be drawn up. It shows the relationships between all the members of a group under study. The most similar members are grouped together. The phylogeny explicitly assumes that the more similar members of the group evolved more recently, branching off from the same common ancestors. This process has been revolutionised by the analysis of the genetic code: it is now possible to compare the composition of the genetic code and determine the likely number of molecular changes to get from one type of organism to the next. In this way, it has been possible to show that humans are more closely related to chimpanzees than they are to gorillas. In addition, because the average rate of change of the genetic code can be calculated and checked against the dating of fossil species, it is possible to estimate the time of branching between two closely related species. In the case of humans and chimpanzees, the estimate is about 5–6 million years from branch point A (Figure 1.17(a)). In other words, it is likely that an ancestor of both chimps and humans existed, somewhere in Africa, about 6 million years ago. Similarly, it is possible to trace back all the insects to a single common ancestor about 400 million years ago. Indeed, because the genetic code of all living organisms can be compared, it is possible to determine when the last ancestor of any two named groups occurred and how any one species is related to any other species. In this way the whole tree of life can now be understood. Charles Darwin, who in his book *On the Origin of Species* set out his theory of evolution that explained how all living organisms have a common ancestry, could hardly have imagined that our knowledge would have advanced so far in 150 years to produce such an intricate and full mapping of the tree of life. His initial and tentative attempts to sketch species branching and generating new species can be seen in Figure 1.17(b).

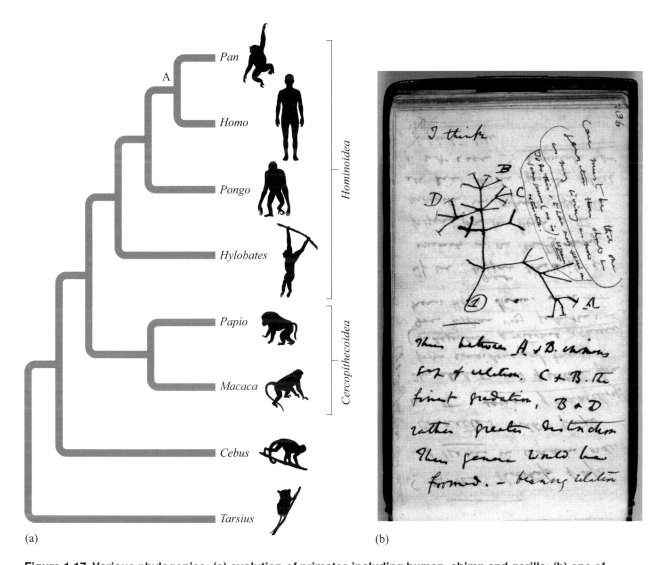

(a)   (b)

Figure 1.17 Various phylogenies: (a) evolution of primates including human, chimp and gorilla; (b) one of Darwin's sketches

5.2   Identifying a new species

When scientists observe organisms in the wild, or in a museum collection, they look for characteristics that match those of species already described by others. The scientist might use drawings, sound recordings, photographs, preserved specimens, tissue samples, and even behavioural features of the organism to compare with other organisms. If the organism does not seem to match any known species, the scientist writes a description highlighting the observed differences that have led the scientist to conclude that it is actually a separate species, i.e., that it is evolving independently from other species. The description introduces a new two-part name in Latin for the species, and has to be published to become valid. New observations test the validity of a species description over time, sometimes finding that what was described as a new species is in fact a different sex or life stage of another species. These cases are rare, though, and most species descriptions stand the test of time quite well. Even in today's increasingly interconnected world, our knowledge of species in the tropics lags far behind our understanding of the composition of Martian soil, for instance. This is true even for relatively well-studied animals, such as mammals. Over the last decade about 140 new mammal species have been described in South America.

In the study of mountain gorillas in Bwindi in Block 3 Part 2, the gorillas are referred to as one of two sub-species of the Eastern gorilla species. Moreover, there are two separate populations of mountain gorillas (*Gorilla beringei beringei*): those you have studied in Bwindi in Uganda, and another population in the Virungas that straddle Rwanda, Democratic Republic of Congo and Uganda. Most of our knowledge of mountain gorillas is derived from research carried out at Karisoke in Rwanda, and thus on the mountain gorillas of the Virungas. However, since scientific research of the Bwindi mountain gorillas began in the 1990s, it has been suggested that the Bwindi mountain gorilla is a different sub-species of the Eastern gorilla. This is in part based on the slightly different look of the two populations of mountain gorillas (Virunga mountain gorillas live at higher elevations and have longer body hair than the Bwindi mountain gorillas) and their different diets (Virunga mountain gorillas eat largely bamboo and few fruits, while Bwindi gorillas eat little bamboo and lots of fruit). While no decision has yet been taken, research is continuing to determine whether there is sufficient difference between these two populations of mountain gorillas to warrant a reclassification, with the Bwindi population being classified as a third sub-species of the Eastern gorilla (Royal Belgian Institute of Natural Sciences, n.d.).

This example demonstrates that while there is a scientifically accepted process of classifying species, debate and disagreement do occur. This is because the taxonomy of species is a human classification system. As such, it is a construct that is overlaid on the biological world. However, the application of genetic coding is making taxonomy more scientifically robust and less open to subjective interpretation.

As you will see later, in Section 7 when we visit the Arawak people of Wakapoa, it is not essential to have this classification system to make sense of and use the forest. The Arawak people manage very well without the aid of Western taxonomy. Indeed, their knowledge system is quite different, but more of this later.

5.3   Biodiversity

The term 'richness' has already been used and suggests the array of different species of organisms in an area. In one sense this is a straightforward inventory – x different species of plant, y different species of animals with four legs, z different species of animals with six legs, and so on. However, scientists are interested not only in the detail of the abundance of different species, but also the richness at different levels of biological organisation. It would be appropriate at this point to further explore the term 'biodiversity', which has already been referred to in Block 1. Biodiversity is the variation of life forms within a given ecosystem or other area of study or even the entire planet, and is derived from the two words *biology* and *diversity*.

It is important not to confuse biodiversity with just 'wildlife' as the term is used in Part 2 of Block 3. Literally, wild life should refer to any organisms that are not specifically managed by and for human use. But it has sometimes assumed a much more restricted use, to refer to a particular group of species that are iconic or inhabit particularly spectacular landscapes, for example gorillas in Bwindi and polar bears in the Arctic. Insects are in the strictest sense of the term 'wildlife', with the possible exception of honey bees and silk moths, but there are considerably more insects than there are gorillas and polar bears, and insects are everywhere. This is one reason why scientists strive to define their terms as rigorously as possible. In that way communication is clearer and unambiguous. It has to be said that biodiversity is not an especially successful example of scientific terminology. In fact, like 'wildlife' and 'environment', it is a word that has been overtaken by popular usage – it is successful in terms of communicating ideas to a wider audience but not sufficiently precise for most scientific study. For now, biodiversity will do as a term, although I may need to occasionally clarify its meaning, and richness will simply refer to the number or variety of different types of living organism.

In Block 1 the term biodiversity was introduced and used in a limited sense to refer to the number of different species. Here I am expanding its meaning to encompass variation at all levels of biological organisation. The three levels at which biological variation has been identified are:

- genetic diversity (the variation in genetic makeup within the same species)
- species diversity (number of different species)
- ecosystem diversity (variation between different ecosystems).

The biodiversity of a region can be defined as the totality of genes, species and ecosystems within that region. You should by now have a reasonable idea of what is meant by variation in species and ecosystems, but we need briefly to consider what is meant by genetic diversity and why it may be important.

5.3.1 Genetic diversity

Genetic diversity refers to the genetic variation that is found within the same species. All members of the same species are alike in most fundamental aspects, such as size, number of legs, spots on wings, etc., using an example of a butterfly. However, there are also identifiable differences between members of the same species, some of which are visible and some that are not. This *genetic variation* within species is evident in the physical variation between individuals – humans are one species but they all look different. The exception to the rule is 'identical twins', which are the product of one egg and one sperm, i.e. the product of the same set of genes from the two parents. Because physical features are not wholly determined by genes, even 'identical' twins may not look identical. It is important to appreciate that a species, whether it be humans, jaguars or a particular tree species, contains variation in its genetic composition.

Genetic variation within a species is very important, as it can provide a mechanism for species survival should conditions in the environment change. As there is genetic variation within any particular species then it is possible that a few members of that species are, by chance, more suited to survival when changes occur in their environment. Genetic variation within a species is also the basis of how evolution of species over very long periods of time occurs by the process of *natural selection*.

SAQ 1.1 Biodiversity and conservation

1   Explain in your own words the difference between biodiversity and wildlife.

2   Write a couple of sentences explaining how biodiversity incorporates different levels of natural variation.

   Hint: Think about the three different levels of organisation of biodiversity discussed above. You may also need to refer back to the discussion of what conservation is in Block 3 Part 2.

Summary of Section 5

Biodiversity is a measure of the variety of life that exists on Earth. We commonly think primarily of species diversity, especially with respect to charismatic wildlife, but biodiversity should be considered at three different levels: genetic, species and ecosystem.

The variety of life in Amazonia

6

6.1 Why is Amazonia so diverse?

Amazonia has become emblematic of the richness of tropical forests and of the rapid changes that such areas are undergoing around the world as a result of human intervention. This contemporary symbol, however, fails to convey the reality of diverse habitats where change has been the only constant for millions of years. Indeed, now and in the past, some of the most extraordinary species have lived in the Amazonian savannahs outside the forest.

The savannah is home to the largest living rodent, the capybara. Rodents are a group of related species that include rats and mice. Capybaras weigh up to 80 kg and occur in various types of savannah and wetland, generally near rivers. They tend to move in social groups which may number 30 or more. Although impressive in size, this species is rather small compared with the largest known rodents from fossil remains (Figure 1.18). In 2003, bones of a giant rodent found in the north of Venezuela were described in a scientific paper. Estimation of body mass from the teeth and bones of this species showed that it was about 700 kg, about the size of a well-grown dairy cow! (Amos, 2003). A more recent discovery, in 2007, was of an even larger species south of Amazonia in present-day Uruguay. This species is estimated to have reached 1000 kg in size (Fildes, 2008).

The reduced stature of existing species compared with recently extinct ancestors is a theme that runs across different groups of Amazonian species. Ancestors of the sloths, which were restricted to the ground because of their enormous size, rivalled the African elephant in dimensions and mass. The extinction of these massive ground sloths occurred over millions of years, with the most recent within the last 10 000 years. The cause of extinction is uncertain, although it probably included climate change, which also resulted in shifting patterns of savannah and forest, and, more recently, hunting during the migration of early peoples into North and South America from Asia.

The natural history of Amazonia begins about 90 million years ago, as South America drifted away from Africa to finally break apart the ancient supercontinent of Gondwana (see the discussion of plate tectonics in Block 2, Part 2, Section 3). As South America moved west, it crashed against the Pacific plate, lifting the western edge of the continent and eventually forming the Andes mountain chain. These emerging mountains in the west, and the Guiana shield in the north, framed the vast tropical lowlands of South America that comprise Amazonia. (Shields, such as the Guiana shield, are very ancient areas of mountain and rock.) Just as a rug crumples if pushed from the side, parts of Amazonia became folded hundreds of miles east of the edge of impact between the Pacific and South American

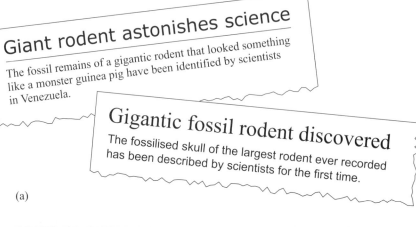

Giant rodent astonishes science

The fossil remains of a gigantic rodent that looked something like a monster guinea pig have been identified by scientists in Venezuela.

Gigantic fossil rodent discovered

The fossilised skull of the largest rodent ever recorded has been described by scientists for the first time.

(a)

(b)

Figure 1.18 Large rodents in South America: (a) BBC press headlines on the discoveries and descriptions of giant rodents in South America; (b) the largest extant rodent, the capybara

plates. Although these ridges barely register today, the relief they formed millions of years ago established drainage patterns and soil types that influence life today. The upheaval of plates colliding produced a geography of north-western South America that we would not recognise. Until about 8 million years ago the upper Amazon and Orinoco rivers flowed north and drained into the Caribbean Sea. As another thrust of uplift raised the Cordillera Oriental of the Andes in north-western South America, the Orinoco and Amazon split apart and shifted course to the east, acquiring their current orientation, so that South America became a giant island.

The plants and animals that persisted after the break-up, or reached the continent by drifting, swimming or flying to it, then evolved in what the palaeontologist George Gaylord Simpson called 'splendid isolation', until the closing of the Isthmus of Panama around 4 million years ago formed a new land link with North America. What Simpson considered splendid about this isolation was the prevalence of organisms endemic to South America, meaning that they were not found on any other continent. Some of these might be familiar to us, for example the three-toed sloth of Figure I.1, while others strain the imagination; as noted above, the extinct relatives of this small sloth were the size of elephants. The results of isolation are nowhere as diverse and colourful as in Amazonia (Figure 1.19). Under the canopy of tall trees in upland Amazonia there are ovenbirds, tyrant flycatchers, manakins and woodcreepers, all birds without close

(a)

(b)

(c)

Figure 1.19 A small sample of Amazonian diversity: (a) yellow-banded dart frog (*Dendrobates leucomelas*); (b) passion vine (*Passiflora* sp.); (c) *Theraphosa blondi* (the world's largest spider, often the size of a dinner plate)

relatives outside South America. Attached to the trees there are moss-like flowering plants related to the pineapple that obtain their nutrients and water from the air. Up in the branches, jumping and scurrying from one clump of fruits to the next, various monkey species forage methodically. These are the descendants of a primate ancestor that reached South America from Africa (possibly on rafts of vegetation) about 35 million years ago, long after the break-up of Gondwana. Today, more species of New World monkeys are found in Amazonia than in all other regions of the continent combined.

SAQ 1.2   Measures of biodiversity

What measure of biodiversity is referred to in the paragraph above?

Is it:

- species diversity (number of different species)
- genetic diversity (the variation in genetic makeup within the same species)
- ecosystem diversity (variation between different ecosystems)?

The great biodiversity of Amazonia has inspired many explanations for how the many species arose. One important feature is *geographical isolation*. You have already seen how the whole of South America was isolated for many millions of years. Within South America there was further isolation of different regions owing to the patterns of river flow and mountain formation. Areas that have high degrees of isolation, such as islands surrounded by ocean, often have high numbers of endemic species, as the example of Hawaii in Block 1 showed. Madagascar, a large island off the south-east coast of Africa, is a good example of an island that has been isolated for many millions of years and within which there is a high number of endemic species. Like Amazonia, and especially certain parts of it, such as western Peru, Madagascar is valued because those species are found nowhere else.

When discussing Amazonian biodiversity most references in both popular and science articles refer to the number of different species. Indeed, it is the sheer number of different trees, vines, beetles, rodents, monkeys, birds, butterflies, etc. found in Amazonia that has impressed visitors for centuries. Although the concept of species is a hotly debated topic in biology, the determination and description of species is relatively straightforward, which is why abundance – the number of different species – is the most commonly used measure of biodiversity.

6.2   Biodiversity case study

As an introduction to the richness of the Amazonian tropical forest and as a means of understanding the classification of species further, I am going to spend some time discussing butterflies. Butterflies are found in all but the harshest environments on Earth. In the tropics, they are found in lowland forests, savannahs and cloud forests. The numbers of species are highest in tropical forests, especially in gaps or forest edges or at the top of the canopy. The study of butterflies in tropical regions has several advantages. First, unlike most other insect groups, many of them can be easily identified, often just by the patterns on their wings. Second, they have a strong link to other components of the ecosystem, especially plants. The linkage to plants occurs at two stages in their life cycle (Figure 1.20). The larvae (caterpillars) feed on particular species of plant whilst the adults may take nectar from a flower or feed on fruit. The adults may also take nutrients from non-plant sources including animal dung!

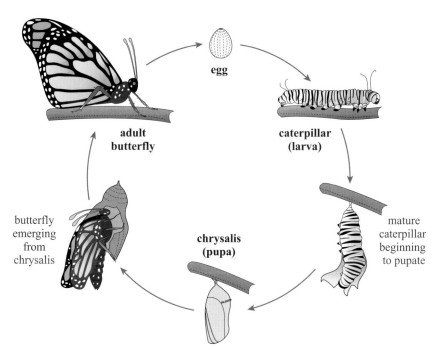

Figure 1.20 Life cycle of a butterfly. All butterflies share the same life cycle, albeit with different durations for each of the four life-cycle stages (life-cycle stages in bold)

But what is a butterfly? 'It's an insect with colourful wings' is the simple answer. But what is an insect? And surely there are other insects with colourful wings? Plainly, the answer is not quite that simple. However, with a little work, a definition of a butterfly can be reached so that you can proceed to explore the richness of these beautiful creatures.

To start with, an *insect* needs to be defined. This is an animal that, as an adult, has a body in three parts: a head, a thorax (to which the legs are attached) and an abdomen. Fossil records show that insects have existed for over 300 million years. During that time evolution has produced a remarkable array of forms, of which butterflies are a relatively recent arrival. Most insects live all or part of their lives on land – there are very few marine insects. The different insect groups include beetles, dragonflies and scorpion flies. Some of these groups have evolved many different species; for example, beetles comprise over 300 000 species (about a tenth of all known species of any type on Earth) whilst others, such as scorpion flies, look much the same today as they did when they first appeared over 250 million years ago in the Permian period (Figure 1.21). A famous remark, attributed to the biologist J.B.S. Haldane, was the response to a question about what could be inferred about the Creator from his many works. His answer was 'an inordinate fondness for beetles'!

(a)   (b)

Figure 1.21 Examples of insects: (a) fossil scorpion fly; (b) scorpion fly

One of the challenges for evolutionary biologists is to understand how the various insects are related to each other. Are butterflies more similar to beetles or to scorpion flies? For about the first 150 years of this work the emphasis was on the structure of the insects. Entomologists (people who study insects) concentrated on structures such as the halteres of a fly, which are modified wings. By placing all insects with halteres in one group they defined the true flies and gave them the scientific name of Diptera (meaning two wings). By comparing the presence or absence of particular structures across insect groups, entomologists worked out how similar or different insect groups were. In this way a classification of insects was arrived at (you were introduced to the process of classification in Block 1). For example, one of the most fundamental differences between insects is whether, as adults, they possess wings or not. It is generally assumed that the earliest types of insect did not have wings and that, over time, some groups of insects evolved wings. A complication here is that some of those insects whose ancestors had wings then lost them again! To identify an insect you need to go through a key that asks about particular structures. A key to identify butterflies would read something like this (assuming that you know it is an insect):

1 Does it have wings? (Of course, if you do not have an adult specimen then you cannot proceed to this point!)

Answer: yes or no. This form of *dichotomous key*, i.e. with two answers, is very popular.

If the answer is yes, then proceed to Question 2. (If the answer is no you would be sent to a different part of the key, which is not included here.)

2 Does it have two or four wings?

Answer: two or four.

If the answer is four, then proceed to Question 3.

3 Are the wings highly coloured or at least continuously covered with coloured scales?

Answer: yes or no.

If the answer is yes, then proceed to Question 4.

4 Does it have clubbed or feathery antennae? (See Figure 1.22.)

If the answer is clubbed, it is a butterfly and if the answer is feathery (or at least, not clubbed), it is a moth (Figure 1.22).

(a)

(b)

Figure 1.22 Butterfly identification: (a) distinction between moth and butterfly antennae; (b) butterfly identification in Nicaragua

Once you know it is a butterfly you can carry on looking at more and more detailed structures, but you can also simply look at pictures of butterflies. There are now many good butterfly identification books that allow easy identification in the field. This means that there is often no need to take specimens from the field. Activity 1.3 gives you an opportunity to try this yourself.

Activity 1.3   Using the key to identify butterflies

Look at the four pictures of insects in Figure 1.23 and use the key to identify which of these are butterflies and which are moths.

(a)

(b)

(c)

(d)

Figure 1.23 A selection of insects

Discussion

Photos (a) and (c) are butterflies; (d) is a moth because it does not have clubbed antennae and (b) is neither a moth nor a butterfly because it has only two wings. From using the key that is all you can say, but in fact it is a crane fly.

So insects include a diverse set of organisms, including butterflies, beetles and true flies. This organisation of insects, like all other organisms, is described by the various levels of classification (Box 1.3, Block 1). Insects are placed at the level of class (class Insecta). Insecta is included with other classes such as the Malacostraca (which includes crabs, lobsters, shrimps and woodlice) in the phylum Arthropoda. The phylum Arthropoda is included with other phyla such as Chordata (which includes all the vertebrates) in the kingdom Animalia. Within a given class, different orders are recognised, such as beetles (order Coleoptera), butterflies and moths (order Lepidoptera) and true flies (order Diptera). Within each order, different families are recognised, such as the families Nymphalidae and Pieridae in the butterflies. Finally, each family contains one or more genera, which themselves may have one or more different species.

The previous paragraph is a very rapid summary of a complex and dense subject. You do not need to remember the detail here, but students of biology in the past would have been expected to recite the various levels of organisation, perhaps using an aide-memoire such as the mnemonic 'Keep Pots Clean Or Family Gets Sick' or the more racy 'King Philip Came Over For Good Sex', which stand for the levels of Kingdom, Phylum, Class, Order, Family, Genus and Species. In fact, it is generally unnecessary to recall these levels and various examples of them. I happen to remember the families of butterflies and many plants because I have undertaken research on them; but it would be just as easy to look the names up in a book or online.

Summary of Section 6

The history of Amazonia over geological time has resulted in it exhibiting very high species diversity. To study this we need to be able to identify different species using the science of taxonomy, which groups different organisms in a hierarchical sequence. Using dichotomous keys, it is possible to identify a given organism to the species level, illustrated by the case of butterflies.

7   Amazonia's human inhabitants

Having looked at the biodiversity of Amazonia, we now turn to look at the species that has wrought the greatest change in Amazonia: humans. In this final section of Part 1, the traditional interactions of people with the forest and savannah will be described. This will illustrate the essential ingredients of people's everyday lives, repeated across wide areas of Amazonia. Many of the intimate associations and dependencies between indigenous peoples and their natural environment are being lost and replaced with modern features such as outboard motors and DVD players. Recent transitions in life for people in Amazonia have been swift and not always positive.

7.1   Colonisation

There have been two main waves of human colonisation in Amazonia. The first wave started at least 9000 years ago with the arrival of people from Asia crossing the Bering Strait to North America. They settled throughout North and South America, from the northernmost ice-covered regions of the Arctic to the southernmost tip of South America via the Andes and Amazonia. There is considerable debate over the exact dates of arrival in Amazonia of these people from Asia, and indeed whether there were any other colonisation routes. But these settlers from Asia who made up the first wave of colonisation generated some of the most extraordinary civilisations of the world, including the Incas, Mayans and Aztecs. Note that the term Amerindian is used for indigenous peoples of North and South America. However, the term is not universally favoured by the people themselves, who prefer to be called indigenous or first nations, or by the name of their particular group or tribe, for example the Inuit you met in Block 2.

The second wave of human colonisation began in the late fifteenth century with Europeans, principally from Spain, Portugal, Netherlands and Britain, settling land throughout the Americas. The archaeological evidence from the first and second waves of colonisation is often distinguished as pre-Columbian (i.e. before the arrival of Columbus in the Caribbean in 1492) and Columbian. This second wave of colonisation led to major changes for the existing indigenous peoples, many of which were highly damaging. Persecution and religious intolerance by the colonising powers led to loss of lands and rights of communities and whole civilisations, whilst an unintended consequence of colonisation was the introduction of killer diseases to which the indigenous people had no immunity. Smallpox killed about half of the indigenous population of Hispaniola, with between 60 and 90% of Incas being lost owing to the same disease (Cook, 1998).

But the colonisers of the second wave flourished. Ultimately, the colonies sought independence from the European colonial powers in the nineteenth and twentieth centuries. One of the legacies left by the colonial powers was their language, with the independent countries of South America mainly speaking Spanish, although in Brazil Portuguese is spoken. Many indigenous languages do persist, albeit with reduced usage amongst their peoples.

Any one country may have a variety of indigenous languages. For example, whilst English is spoken as the official language in Guyana (as it was previously British Guiana), it also includes twelve indigenous languages. The two other Guianas were colonised by the Dutch (Dutch Guiana became Surinam) and the French (remaining French Guiana, Figure 1.24).

7.2   Today's peoples of the forest

In this subsection you will be introduced to some of Amazonia's people. You will learn about how they live in the forest and begin to understand some of the environmental issues facing indigenous people today. This will be done through text and films and a focus on one community, the Arawak of Wakapoa in Guyana (see Figure 1.25). There are 14 short films of a few minutes each on a range of topics affecting the people of Wakapoa. These address broad themes including transport, agriculture, and use of medicinal plants. But not all of the material needs to be viewed here. Suggestions of appropriate places to view it will be made as we go through the text, but you are welcome to dip in when you feel like it.

The community of Wakapoa is located over many small islands within a wetland area. The administrative centre is based on an island about 0.5 miles in diameter and contains a school, health centre, church, village council office and about ten homes. There are major changes in the level of water from wet to dry season, but it is never dry like the savannah grassland described in Section 3. The community is only accessible via a small creek through a gap in the mangrove forest alongside the Pomeroon river. The nearest town, Charity, is about 30 miles upriver from the community. The Atlantic Ocean is approximately five miles away. The islands of the community occur on various substrates, including fine white sand. There are areas that support high mature forest, although logging and cassava farming occur on many islands. The total population of the community is over 2000.

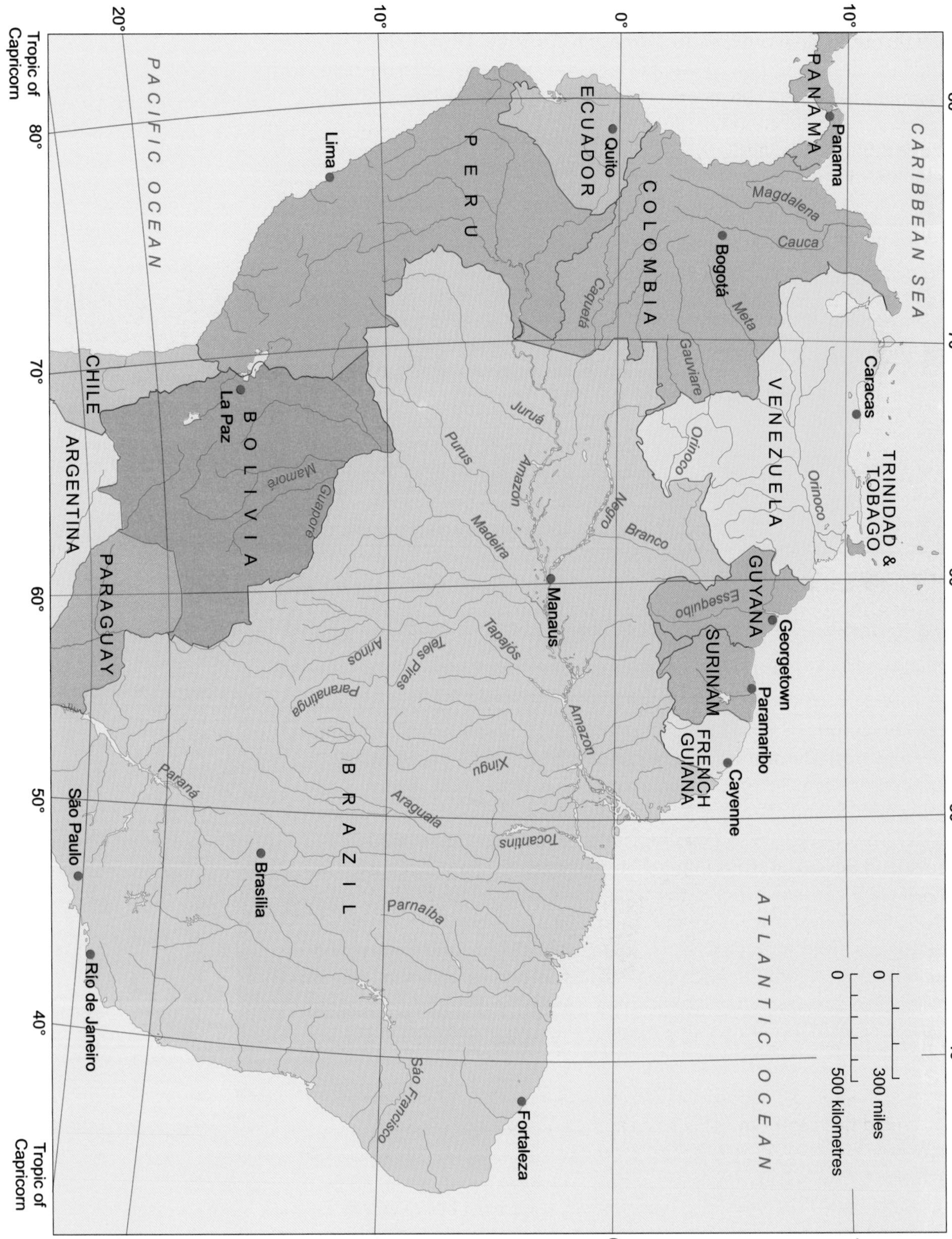

Figure 1.24 Map of Amazonia showing national borders (*Source: Mountain High®*)

The community is composed primarily of Arawak people. This is true of neighbouring communities too, although Carib and Warau people also live in the north-west region of Guyana and there is much intermarriage. Arawaks and Caribs are widely distributed through the Guianas and tropical South America. The Arawak, Carib and Warau languages belong to three different families (groups) of languages. But keeping the languages alive is a major problem. In Wakapoa few people under the age of 40 speak Arawak, although people over 50 are generally fluent or conversant in it.

(a)   (b)

(c)

Figure 1.25 People and places in Wakapoa: (a) a domestic scene; (b) a group of residents; (c) local children

A strong dependence on their surroundings for shelter and food has provided this community with an intimate knowledge of their environment. This knowledge includes the calls of birds, the taste, structure and smell of plants, the flow of the river and signals of the changing seasons. They have learnt the uses of many different plants for construction, food and medicine. A couple of examples of living in a forest environment will be now be explored.

Activity 1.4   Introducing the people of Wakapoa

I suggest that you begin by watching the following short (1–2 minutes each) video sequences on the DVD: Introduction, Cassava, Music, Language, Basil, Samantha and Vera. These provide an overview of the place and the people and insights into their perceptions. You should compile notes on the programmes under the following headings: livelihood, culture, and change.

Discussion
The following notes are placed under three headings, but some of the points straddle the headings and could be put under another heading or under more than one.

Livelihood
the approximately 2000 people from Wakapoa live on a collection of many small islands

cassava is the traditional carbohydrate staple food which has to be farmed

fish that have to be caught are eaten with cassava

forest cleared by slash and burn to grow cassava

people farmed to live and earn money

Vera, although old now, still farming – says it's very hard work.

Culture
there are a school, health centre and council offices in the community

cassava preparation involves many stages and traditional methods handed down the generations

few speak the indigenous language now (which is likely to result in loss of folklore, traditions, etc.)

changes in music – results in changes in entertainment and social cohesion

Basil has been away and can now return because he has been away, says the forest 'catch me' to return

Wakapoa seems boring to a young person (Samantha).

Change
few speak the language now, only older members, young can speak a few words only

20 years ago traditional music, now big CD player

in Wakapoa transport by boat, livelihood by farming – very hard work for women who have to clean, collect children from school, etc.

in town, away from Wakapoa – internet, city culture, transport any time, light, tv.

7.3   Buildings

Traditionally, homes were built from local timber with palm leaves for roofing (Figure 1.26(a)) and may be built on stilts to allow for seasonal flooding. Transport was either by foot or in dugout canoes paddled through creeks and along the edges of rivers. Canoes could be hauled overland at rapids. A great deal of local knowledge was involved in sourcing wood for houses and canoes. The most suitable trees may have grown some distance away and often not in the same place. Palm-leaf roofing may last a few years before needing to be replaced. Today, the preference is for corrugated iron roofs. These are longer lasting and less attractive to a range of undesirable inhabitants such as rats and cockroaches, but have the disadvantages of being hot during the day and very noisy when it rains.

(a)

(b)

Figure 1.26 Traditional building: (a) interior of a school building in a small indigenous community along the Rio Caura (central Venezuela) – the roof is made from palm leaves; (b) dugout canoe construction

Dugout canoes are traditionally made from one tree. A suitably sized tree is cut down, the bark removed and the log is roughly shaped by removing a third to one-half of the width, and the centre (sometimes with the aid of fire; see Figure 1.26(b)). The rough-shaped log is then heated over a low fire for several days to dry it and to allow it to be prised open to the required final shape.

7.4   Cassava: a staple food of the poor

Cassava (*Manihot esculenta*) is the traditional source of carbohydrate for indigenous people in tropical South America and continues to be the dominant source of carbohydrate (the staple food) for many rural people (Figure 1.27). The plant is native to South America but was introduced to west Africa by the Portuguese in the sixteenth century and thereafter to Sri Lanka in 1786 and Java in 1835 (Lotschert and Beese, 1981). Cassava has become established as an important food source in west and central Africa and South-East Asia, where it is also known as manioc and tapioca. It is estimated that over 500 million people worldwide depend on cassava – or nearly 10% of the global population. An important feature of cassava, and one that has driven much ingenuity, is that most varieties can be highly toxic in their raw form and therefore require processing before consumption.

The following discussion of cassava is quite detailed. The reason for this is that it is a good example of how a single natural resource, a plant, binds a human society together, encourages co-operation, has heavily influenced social development and affected that society's attitude to the natural environment.

(a)   (b)

Figure 1.27 (a) Cassava plant; (b) prepared tubers

Origins of cassava

The origins of cassava seem to be in the south-west of Brazil about 8000 years ago. From here it spread northwards, with the first archaeological evidence about 7500 BP (before present) from the Porce valley in north-west Colombia. The origin and dispersal of the other major indigenous carbohydrate source of the **Neotropics** (the tropical regions of Central and South America), maize (*Zea mays*), appears to have occurred in the opposite direction, i.e., from Central America southwards. Although maize was probably the dominant food plant in Central America, with recorded ages of first use of more than 7500 years ago, both plants were being used in Central America over 5000 years ago. Analysis of tiny plant remains (starch grains) from Panama provide evidence of cassava directly linked to the stone tools used for their processing. In this case the plant remains were found on a flake chopper dated to about 5600 BP and a grinding stone base dated to about 3600 BP (Dickau et al., 2007). Thus, the evidence is of about 8000 years of continuous usage of cassava across the continent, with a discovery time similar to that of maize, and subsequent rapid dispersal.

At least five of the carbohydrate sources in current cultivation can also be found in archaeological records from over 3500 years ago. These crops also feature in the records of indigenous peoples outside the Neotropics. For example, the New Zealand Maori brought their food plants from East Polynesia about 900 years ago (Irwin, 1992; Harris, 2006), including *Ipomoea batatas* (sweet potato), which is their main food plant, and *Dioscorea* species (yams). As *Ipomoea* does not feature in the archaeological records it may be that this is a more recent introduction to South America (although it is recorded from pre-Columbian sites in Peru (Lotschert and Beese, 1981)).

A recent census of farms of different size in Brazilian Amazonia showed cassava to be the most important crop in farms of less than 100 hectares (Simon and Garagorry, 2005).

How cassava is grown

Cassava is generally grown under slash-and-burn agriculture, in which small plots of forest are cleared using axes and similar tools. The slashed vegetation is burnt to release nutrients such as potassium and phosphorus stored in the plant back into the soil (although nitrogen is lost in the process) and thereafter 'sticks' (parts of the cassava stem) are planted. The plants are grown for about 12–18 months and the tubers harvested at the end of this period, when the plants are about 1.5–2 m high. Other crops are planted in these fields but rarely achieve the abundance of cassava.

How cassava is eaten

Indigenous people in Central and South America use cassava in a variety of ways, including making a dry wafer-like 'bread', a nutty-textured cereal (farine), a mildly alcoholic drink (parakari) and a sticky sauce used in cooking (cassareep). The plants are divided into 'sweet' and 'bitter' varieties which are classified according to the levels of toxins they contain. Sweet varieties contain relatively small amounts of toxin so their tubers can be cooked like potato or yam. Bitter varieties, which tend to have larger tubers, cannot be treated in this way and need to be processed to remove the toxins that are naturally present in the plant.

How cassava is prepared

After harvesting, the tubers are grated and then put into a device that squeezes out the juice containing much of the toxic substances. This juice can be boiled to form the sticky cooking sauce. Traditionally the cassava was grated on handmade graters which contained thousands of tiny fragments of stone forced into a board. Indigenous tribes such as the Wai-Wai in the south of Guyana became expert in making these graters and traded them widely:

> She was making one of the cassava graters for which, since the earliest times, her tribe had been famous. Following rough black guide lines painted by her husband, who had fashioned the rectangular board of soft wood, she hammered tiny chips of stones – five or six thousand to each grater – into its surface, each into a previously punched crack. When she had finished, the grater would be painted by her husband with vermilion paint mixed with latex to hold the chips in, and decorated with a design in black: the ends and back with stylized zig-zag patterns, the centre of the front with a simpler, more carefully executed motif, perhaps of an alligator, a monkey, a cross, or a collection of dots.

(Guppy, 1958)

Long-distance trading and local specialisation in crafts or certain plant products was a traditional feature of the lives of indigenous people, for example seen clearly in the distribution of products used in the processing of curare and blowpipes (Schomburgk, 1840). Today, one of the few remaining cultural connections is through the products of cassava processing (Figure 1.28). This is typified by the device that is used to extract the cassava juice. This beautifully designed implement, known as a matape, which means snake (specifically a constricting type of snake), is woven from a particular palm species, which is also used for the sieve. As the matape lengthens it constricts the contents, forcing out the toxic juices. The resulting 'meal' shows the constriction marks (Figure 1.28(c)). Along with clearing the land, matape construction is the only part of the process for which the men are responsible. The cultivation, grating and cooking of cassava is the traditional work of the women.

(a)

(b)

(c)

(d)

Figure 1.28 Essential components of cassava production: (a) plant growing from sticks in the ground; (b) a matape, used for squeezing juice from plants; (c) cassava after squeezing in a matape; (d) drying

The sophistication of the processes involved in cassava utilisation is well illustrated by the production of parakari (Henkel, 2005). The process recorded by Henkel involved 30 steps divided into six phases and a dual fermentation process, the first of which involves a fungus (*Rhizopus* sp.). Henkel's study in Aishalton in south-west Guyana demonstrated the use of 37 varieties of cassava, two of which were sweet and therefore could be used directly for cooking tubers, with the remaining 35 bitter varieties used for parakari, bread or farine. Twenty varieties were used for parakari, of which 16 were used also for bread and/or farine. Of the four varieties used only for parakari, three were observed to ferment slowly.

The first phase of parakari production is the same as cassava bread manufacture, except that the bread is cooked slightly more than usual. The second phase involves the use of *Trema micrantha* leaves, which carry the *Rhizopus* fungus. The leaves are dried, powdered and mixed with starch from cassava to prepare a fungal inoculum. In the third phase the cassava bread is soaked in water and layered with the fungal inoculum between *Heliconia* leaves. The first stage of fermentation is during phase four, in which the *Rhizopus* fungi grow extensively through the layered cassava bread. After about 48 hours the resulting sweet cassava cake may be consumed, with the remainder transferred to airtight containers for alcohol fermentation (phase five). The final phase is consumption!

Genetic variation in cassava plants

The high number of varieties of cassava described by Henkel is not untypical of Amazonia. A comparison of diversity of varieties in north-west Amazonia found an average of 16–33 varieties per informant, with a total number of varieties of between 60 and 89 (Emperaire and Peroni, 2007), whilst a second study in Guyana recorded cultivation of 76 varieties (Elias et al., 2001). Overall, studies of genetic diversity of cassava demonstrate a higher level of genetic diversity than commercial varieties of cassava. These and similar studies discussed the importance of cultural knowledge and social practice in maintenance of the genetic diversity. For example, at marriage, women receive a stock of varieties from their own mother and their mother-in-law. Conversely, the knowledge of matape manufacture is passed through the male lineages. The maintenance of genetic diversity in cassava is seen as a clear product of human selection fostered by a close knowledge of the environment and cultural practices over thousands of years. That it remains intact highlights the importance of the food plant to these people. However, other indigenous knowledge has been lost. There is wide variation in the use of fruits, for example, and overall there is a declining level of fruit processing and consumption. This is indicative of a loss of knowledge about plants in general. Few indigenous people now know about the medicinal properties of plants. This loss of knowledge will be further explored in Part 3.

Cassava – social glue of indigenous communities

This discussion has demonstrated that cassava preparation is a complex, lengthy and highly social process. It has stimulated specialisation, with some communities becoming expert in producing cassava tools (cassava graters, matapes and sieves). These tools were then traded, building links and interdependence between communities. The gender division of work around the processing of cassava is clearly defined, further binding communities together. Moreover, cassava production demands detailed knowledge of toxicity, fermentation and suitable growing conditions. The intricacy and complexity of the process has encouraged interaction between different communities to improve the process. This knowledge is often not written down (written knowledge is called codified knowledge) but is communicated orally between communities (and is called tacit knowledge).

There is a tendency in the developed world to think of knowledge derived from scientific methods as superior to knowledge generated from practice and crafts among the peoples of the developing world. You have been introduced to the former through the discussion of taxonomy and phylogeny, and the latter through the processing of cassava. I hope this discussion has encouraged you to revisit your view of knowledge and appreciate that forms of knowledge other than that generated through scientific method have validity and value.

Activity 1.5   Indigenous communities and their use of the forest

Use the information from Section 7 and its DVD material to write notes on the following:

1   Identify ways in which indigenous communities make use of the forest.

2   Take one or two examples from your answer to Question 1 to illustrate how indigenous knowledge is needed to take advantage of the products of the forest.

3   Discuss possible impacts of indigenous communities on their environment.

Discussion

1   Indigenous communities use the forest for shelter (construction), food and transport. They also use plants to provide medicine. Examples include the use of palm leaves for roofing, and trees from which dugout canoes can be constructed. They also rely on the forest to supply the tools they use for hunting, agriculture and food preparation, including blowpipes for hunting (although these are rarely made now) and the leaves of a particular palm for weaving the matape used for squeezing juices from cassava. The forest also provides soil and nutrients for growing crops such as cassava after clearings have been prepared.

2   The main example discussed in Section 7 is the growing of cassava,
    a major source of carbohydrate for many indigenous peoples, and its
    transformation into useful foods and drinks: bread, alcoholic drinks and
    cooking sauce. Indigenous knowledge is clearly needed here at all stages
    of preparation: distinguishing between sweet and bitter (poisonous)
    varieties, using techniques to squeeze the grated cassava to remove its
    poisonous juices, and making use of fungi on the leaves of certain plants
    to allow the juices to be fermented into a non-lethal alcoholic drink.

    In the past the canoe journeys would be guided by the moon and the tide.

    More generally, the inhabitants of Wakapoa depend on an intimate
    knowledge of their local environment, on bird calls, on the taste, smell and
    structure of plants and on the march of its seasons, to find, identify and
    use its resources.

3   The only impact of indigenous communities that is discussed explicitly
    is their maintenance of genetic diversity in cassava, seen as a positive
    development. Removing forest to create clearings to grow crops clearly
    has an impact, but if practised on a small scale with lengthy periods
    between re-use, the disturbance caused may be of a similar scale to
    small-scale natural disturbances and the cleared areas may eventually
    return to something like the previous state. The other impacts of living in
    the forest are hunting of fish and animals, and use of plants and trees for
    construction and tools. Because many peoples have lived in the forest for
    a long time and its overall appearance and makeup seem to have been
    retained, the main overall impact may be to have subtly changed the
    balance of organisms within the forest, but not the existence of the forest.

Summary of Section 7

The human colonisation of Amazonia started about 10 000 years ago
and was followed by invasions of Europeans from Columbus onwards.
The pre-Columbian settlers used the forest environment for buildings,
transport and food. The cultivation of cassava in forest patches over many
generations has helped to feed many people in sub-Saharan Africa and
South-East Asia. Today, the cultivation and processing of cassava is one of
the few remaining cultural links of people with their natural environment
and traditional lifestyles.

Summary of Part 1

Amazonia is revealed as a storehouse of biological diversity. This first part of Block 4 described the different types of ecosystem in Amazonia, and some of the inhabitants of those ecosystems. The components of biodiversity were discussed, highlighting the genetic, species and ecosystem aspects. The isolation of South America is shown to have been a major influence on the generation of biological richness. Human inhabitants of Amazonia were introduced with a discussion of their interactions with the forests and other ecosystems.

In this part of the block Amazonia has been treated as broadly the tropical region of South America. Part 2 is more specifically focused on the area within the Amazon basin. At the end of your journey through Amazonia, in Part 3, you will contemplate a variety of futures for the region.

After completing Part 1 you should be able to:

- recognise the distinction between habitats, communities and ecosystems
- appreciate the nature of the changes that take place within ecosystems and the timescales over which they can occur
- appreciate the biological diversity and richness of Amazonia
- understand the nature and way of life of indigenous peoples of Amazonia and how they use the forest
- appreciate how scientists use terminology and classification systems as study tools to describe and communicate environmental concepts.

Answers to SAQs

SAQ 1.1

1   Wildlife is a colloquial term that people generally use to describe animals such as gorillas, other mammals and birds. In other words, it tends to cover conspicuous, cuddly, furry, feathery or frightening species. Therefore it is a small fraction of the biodiversity of a given area.

2   Biodiversity can be used at the level of genetic variation, variation between species and variation between ecosystems. Each of the higher levels will incorporate variation in the lower level; for example variation between ecosystems will also include variation between species, whilst variation between species also encompasses genetic variation.

SAQ 1.2

Species diversity (number of different species).

References

Amos, J. (2003) 'Giant rodent astonishes science' BBC News, http://news.bbc.co.uk/1/hi/sci/tech/3120950.stm (accessed August 2009)

Attenborough, D. (1956) *Zoo Quest to Guiana*, Cambridge, Lutterworth Press.

Barbier, E.B. (2006) 'Natural barriers to natural disasters: replanting mangroves after the tsunami', *Frontiers in Ecology and the Environment*, vol. 4, pp. 124–31.

Cook, N.D. (1998) *Born to Die: Disease and New World Conquest, 1492–1650*, Cambridge, Cambridge University Press.

Davis, H. (n.d., probably mid 1950s) *The Jungle and the Damned*, London, The Travel Book Club.

Dickau, R., Ranere, A.J. and Cooke, R.G. (2007) 'Starch grain evidence for the preceramic dispersals of maize and root crops into tropical dry and humid forests of Panama', *Proceedings of the National Academy of Sciences*, vol. 104, pp. 3651–56.

Elias, M., Penet, L., Vindry, P., McKey, D., Panaud, O. and Robert, T. (2001) 'Unmanaged sexual reproduction and the dynamics of genetic diversity of a vegetatively propagated crop plant, cassava (*Manihot esculenta* Crantz), in a traditional farming system', *Molecular Ecology*, vol. 10, pp. 1895–1907.

Emperaire, L. and Peroni, N. (2007) 'Traditional management of agrobiodiversity in Brazil: a case study of manioc', *Human Ecology*, vol. 35, pp. 761–68.

Fildes, J. (2008) 'Gigantic fossil rodent discovered' BBC News, http://news.bbc.co.uk/1/hi/sci/tech/7189341.stm (accessed August 2009)

Guppy, N. (1958) *Wai-Wai: Through the Forests North of the Amazon*, New York, Button.

Harris, G. (2006) 'Te Paraiti: The 1905–1906 potato blight epidemic in New Zealand and its effects on Maori communities', The Open Polytechnic of New Zealand, working paper, August 2006.

Henkel, T.W. (2005) 'Parakari, an indigenous fermented beverage using amylolytic *Rhizopus* in Guyana', *Mycologia*, vol. 97, pp. 1–11.

Irwin, G. (1992) *The Prehistoric Exploration and Colonization of the Pacific*, Cambridge, Cambridge University Press.

Lotschert, W. and Beese, G. (1981) Collins Guide to Tropical Plants, London, Collins.

Royal Belgian Institute of Natural Sciences (n.d.) Research: Gorilla agreement website: Conservation Status: *Gorilla berengei beringei*, 'Taxonomy and nomenclature', http://www.naturalsciences.be (Accessed 5 March 2009).

Schomburgk R. (1840) *Richard Schomburgk's Travels in British Guiana, 1840–1844*, translated and edited by W.E. Roth, *Daily Chronicle*, Georgetown, British Guiana (1922–23).

Simon, M.G. and Garagorry, F.L. (2005) 'The expansion of agriculture in the Brazilian Amazon', *Environmental Conservation*, vol. 32, pp. 203–12.

Walton, M.E.M., Samonte-Tan, G.P.B., Primavera, J.H., Edwards-Jones, G. and Le Vay, L. (2006) 'Are mangroves worth replanting? The direct economic benefits of a community-based reforestation project', *Environmental Conservation*, vol. 3, pp. 335–43.

Waterton. C. (1889) *Wanderings in South America*, London, Macmillan (refers to journeys from 1812 to 1824).

Part 2
The Amazon basin

Michael Gillman

Introduction

1

Having considered some of the biodiversity in tropical South America and met some of the people living in a particular location in Guyana, it is now time to zoom out and try to understand some interactions across the whole region. This will provide an opportunity to discuss the role of Amazonia as a contributor to natural processes at a global scale.

The geographical boundary of the African journey in Block 3 was defined in terms of the catchment of the Nile river. The Amazon is another example of an enormous river catchment, comprising 7 million km^2 or about 40% of the total area of South America. This makes it more than twice the size of the Nile catchment. At a length of around 6000 km the maximum distance it covers also rivals that of the Nile. However, it is the discharge (volume of water flowing into the sea) from the Amazon that distinguishes it most from the Nile. The average amount of fresh water flowing from the Amazon is an amazing 219 000 cubic metres per second, about 80 times the amount flowing out of the Nile. Indeed, the Orinoco, although just one quarter of the catchment of the Nile, has a discharge rate of more than ten times that of the Nile.

Wakapoa, the community you met in Part 1, is to the north of the Amazon catchment itself, close to the Essequibo River which runs through the centre of Guyana over a distance of about 1000 km. Although it is 12 miles wide at the mouth, with 365 islands in its delta, the Essequibo catchment is tiny compared with the Amazon and Orinoco (Figure 2.1).

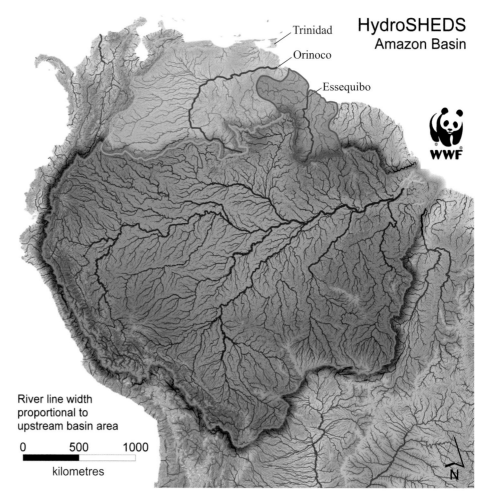

Figure 2.1 Amazon, Orinoco and Essequibo river catchments

Study note: making sense of large numbers

It is easy to imagine lifting 2 kilograms of potatoes, spending £20 or travelling 100 kilometres, but making sense of very large numbers (e.g. trillions of pounds) or unfamiliar units such as a hectare (a unit of area) or a flow of water in cubic metres is more challenging and can get in the way of understanding the story that is being told. A quantity like 219 000 cubic metres per second is very hard to appreciate. But there are techniques you can use to help communicate the significance of size or numbers. You will find them all used in this part (I have already used two above to try to get across the size of the Amazon).

1 *Compare with something similar.* Comparing the flow of water in the Amazon with the Nile (above) showed that the average flow is 80 times higher than that of the Nile. (The size of the Nile was discussed in Block 3.)

2 *Use a striking comparison with a familiar object or quantity*. The water flowing out from the Amazon in *one second* (219 000 cubic metres) would be enough to supply the population of the UK (over 60 million) with their daily water needs for several weeks.

3 Sometimes it may make more sense to *refer to something as a proportion or percentage of a total*, rather than just giving a large number. I used this above by equating 7 million km^2 with 40% (or two fifths) of the total area of South America.

4 *Use an appropriate unit to keep the numbers simple*. Later (Section 2) in this part I discuss the global carbon cycle and movements of very large amounts of this element. Talking about 1×10^{14} kg of carbon can feel very abstract. Using tonnes instead of kilograms can reduce the number (one tonne is 1000 kg). 1×10^{14} kg now becomes, in words, one hundred billion tonnes – still a bit of mouthful – but using the prefix 'giga' to mean a billion allows me to write 1×10^{14} kg of carbon as 100 gigatonnes, or 100 Gt.

5 *Divide a large number into smaller units*. For example, each year humans emit about 7 gigatonnes (or billion tonnes) of carbon into the atmosphere. There are about 7 billion people on the planet. So, the *average* amount emitted per person each year is approximately one tonne of carbon – a much easier number to remember.

Each of these techniques can be useful for putting numbers and quantities in context, but they have to be used carefully to avoid giving a false impression. Scientists usually prefer to stay with scientific notation when discussing large numbers because it is an internationally agreed standard and does not make any assumptions about meaning or interpretation.

To conclude this short introduction, Activity 2.1, which is accessed from the course website, allows you to explore the catchment area of the Amazon by taking a 'virtual' journey along the river.

Activity 2.1   Exploring the Amazon

Go to the U116 course website, select Block 4, Web resources, and click on 'Exploring the Amazon'.

2 Amazonia and the global carbon cycle

2.1 The importance of carbon and its journey

In Block 1 you were introduced to the effects of carbon dioxide on climate change, the carbon cycle and how to calculate your carbon footprint. In Block 2 Part 3 the issue of climate change was picked up again, this time considering the role of methane. In this section the importance of Amazonia in the carbon cycle and its role in global climate change will be explored.

Before launching into the details of the carbon cycle in Amazonia, we need to take a few minutes to review the importance of carbon.

Carbon is found in all organisms. In particular, it is a component of the large molecules (macromolecules) upon which our bodies and the bodies of all organisms, from viruses to elephants, are dependent. The general names of essential macromolecules are probably familiar to you from the ingredients of foodstuffs. These include fats, sugars and proteins. In fact this hides a great deal of detail – there are many different types of fat, whilst sugars is a loose term for just one group of carbohydrates. Carbon is also found in DNA (deoxyribonucleic acid), which holds the genetic code and is one of the two types of nucleic acid found in all cells. All proteins contain carbon, and they perform different functions which can be structural (e.g. in skin cells) or functional (e.g. as enzymes, which help chemical reactions in the body work).

The study of molecules containing carbon is an important branch of chemistry, called organic chemistry. In everyday language the term organic is used in the sense of 'relating to plants and animals', but has been extended to include many human activities or modifications. Organic food or farming mean using only 'natural' techniques and additives, but what exactly is natural? Carbon is not the only element necessary for life, but it is the common factor for organisms. Science fiction writers are fond of the term 'carbon-based life forms', with the implication that there may be other types of life form somewhere outside Earth. In addition to the two elements of water, hydrogen and oxygen, nitrogen is also an essential component of many macromolecules, including DNA. Phosphorus and sulphur are found in others, while sodium, calcium and many trace elements are also essential.

Carbon is thus found in a whole range of different compounds in living organisms, but it is also present in non-living forms, including carbon dioxide, carbonates in rocks and as various carbon-containing fossil fuels. Both fossil fuels and carbonates in rocks are also derived from the bodies or shells of dead organisms. An important question is then how carbon moves between all these various forms.

You may recall from Block 1 that an important process in the movement of carbon involves the action of photosynthesis, which is the making (*synthesis*) of substances using light (*photo*) as an energy source. Photosynthesis occurs in most plants and a few other specialised organisms and involves carbon dioxide (CO_2) from the atmosphere and water being combined to make glucose using light energy from the Sun. The glucose molecules are strung together as **starch** and stored in parts of the plant such as the leaves and roots.

Plants lose this carbon in three ways. First, it can be lost due to respiration by the plant itself. This process involves glucose molecules being split to release energy and producing carbon dioxide and water. This method of respiration is found in most living organisms. The resultant energy is used to drive a whole set of different chemical reactions, collectively referred to as **metabolism**. Second, the carbon in a plant can also be consumed when alive or dead by other organisms and third, it can contribute organic material to the soil where it may be consumed by decomposers. Plant-feeding animals and decomposers will also lose carbon through respiration.

This course is about journeys, and the journey made by carbon is critical. Figure 2.2 shows the journey made by a carbon atom somewhere near Amazonia. Its name is *C*.

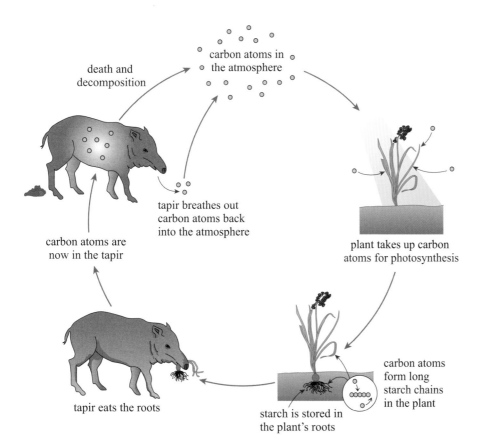

death and decomposition

carbon atoms in the atmosphere

tapir breathes out carbon atoms back into the atmosphere

carbon atoms are now in the tapir

plant takes up carbon atoms for photosynthesis

tapir eats the roots

starch is stored in the plant's roots

carbon atoms form long starch chains in the plant

Figure 2.2 Journey of a carbon atom

Start with C in the atmosphere. During its time in the atmosphere, it may be linked to a couple of oxygen (O) atoms as carbon dioxide, or perhaps four hydrogen (H) atoms as methane. In the former state C might eventually enter a plant and become combined into a starch macromolecule. Imagine that this macromolecule is stored in a plant root for a year or two until it is dug up by a tapir (Figure 2.2), which then consumes the root. From there C travels into the digestive system of the animal, where it is joined by a few fellow atoms in a glucose molecule and enters the bloodstream of the tapir. From here, C may either become incorporated into part of the body of the tapir or be used for energy. C may stay in the tapir for the duration of the animal's life or be expelled in its breath, via its urine or other exudates. Imagine that it stays in the body of the tapir until death. After death, the tapir is fed on by a range of decomposers, which includes insects, fungi and certain bacteria. C may become incorporated into their bodies, or may remain as partially decomposed material in the soil, but at some point it will probably return to the atmosphere as carbon dioxide, or possibly methane, where it began its journey and from where it can continue.

This is just one of many possible journeys that can be taken by C. There are some similarities for each of the journeys:

1   They mostly include time spent in the same types of place such as in the atmosphere, in plants, in animals that feed on plants (herbivores), in animals that feed on animals (decomposers in the case of dead animals or carnivores in the case of live animals), in the non-living part of the soil and in certain rocks. The places where C resides are referred to as *reservoirs* (the same term was used in the water cycle in Block 3). The organisms that make up the living part of the reservoirs (plants, herbivores, carnivores, decomposers) in one particular area comprise a food web (introduced in Part 1).

2   The time spent in each reservoir varies enormously. C may spend years floating in the atmosphere but just a few weeks in a plant or animal. If it gets eaten by a snail and finds itself in the shell of that animal it may be hundreds or thousands of years before it moves on. Similarly, becoming part of the skeleton of a planktonic marine organism may condemn it to millions of years of incarceration in limestone (a carbonate rock). The time spent in a reservoir is referred to as *residence time*.

3   Under normal circumstances on Earth C does not disappear. It will find itself associated with a variety of atomic buddies (O, H and N, nitrogen, for example) but as an atom it persists indefinitely and can travel anywhere in the world, from the atmosphere to the deepest ocean.

4   C is one of an enormous number of fellow travellers, billions upon billions of carbon atoms too numerous to imagine.

Given that there are so many carbon atoms and they travel all over the world and spend different times in each place, how is it possible to make sense of where all the carbon is in the world and how it moves from one place to another? One way is to use the idea of average rates of movement over a given time period between the reservoirs and average residence time to give a summary of the global carbon balance (Figure 2.3). For example, the average rate of movement of carbon from the atmosphere to all plants in the world is known. It is extremely difficult to predict which particular carbon atoms will be incorporated into plants but the overall rate of movement can be estimated. This turns out to be a very large amount: approximately 100 000 000 000 000 kg of C per year, or 1×10^{14} kg. Of course, this number is rather small compared with the number of atoms of carbon. One kilogram of carbon contains a staggering 5×10^{25} atoms (approximately!). So the total number of carbon atoms entering plants from the atmosphere in a year fills a line of text: 5 000 000 000 000 000 000 000 000 000 000 000 000 000 or 5×10^{39}.

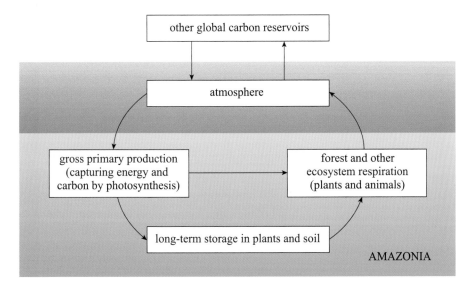

Figure 2.3 Illustration of reservoirs (boxes) and connections between reservoirs (arrows) in part of the global carbon cycle

Study note: multiplying and dividing large numbers

The preceding section gives an example of how to multiply very large numbers using scientific notation: $(1 \times 10^{14}) \times (5 \times 10^{25}) = 5 \times 10^{39}$.

This can be split into two operations: on the numbers and on the multiples or powers of ten.

Multiplying the ordinary numbers is easy: 1×5 is 5.

Multiplying the powers of ten is also not difficult once you can see the pattern. How do you get the answer 39 from 25 and 14? You add the index numbers: $25 + 14 = 39$. That is all there is to it. To multiply powers of ten you simply add the index numbers.

Dividing large numbers follows the same logic. Take the following, simpler example: $3000 / 20 = 150$. Written in scientific notation it becomes $(3 \times 10^3) / (2 \times 10^1) = 1.5 \times 10^2$.

Again, split this into two operations.

First, divide the ordinary numbers: 3 / 2 = 1.5.

Second, divide the powers of ten. How do you get 2 from 3 and 1? This time you subtract the index numbers: 3 − 1 = 2. To divide powers of ten you subtract one index number from the other.

Returning to the issue of movement between the reservoirs, from Figure 2.4 it can be seen that, on average, one-sixth of the carbon in the atmosphere gets incorporated into terrestrial plants and potentially other parts of the food web every year. Understanding these rates of flow will allow a determination of why the amount of carbon in the atmosphere is increasing (this was explored in Block 1).

The term *carbon cycle* is used to describe the movement through the different reservoirs and the storage capacity of each reservoir. The example of the journey of the carbon atom *C* from the atmosphere through the tapir and back to the atmosphere is one example of a carbon cycle. Carbon cycles can be considered at a whole range of different scales, both spatially (for example the global carbon cycle or the carbon cycle of a woodland) and over time. In this section the focus is on the *global* carbon cycle. Although this is a challenging task, study of the global carbon cycle has two advantages. First, the Earth is a *closed system* for carbon, meaning that any carbon atoms stay within the Earth and its atmosphere. There are some exceptions to this, but they are relatively small contributions. In contrast, a woodland may recycle some of its carbon atoms but eventually they will enter the atmosphere and may be lost from that area, or they may enter a stream or river and be carried away. Thus a woodland is an *open system*, at least in some aspects of its function. The second advantage is that, at the global scale, Amazonia can be considered as a single reservoir. This will require a few assumptions along the way, but hopefully you will see the benefit of this global view.

Figure 2.4 summarises the global carbon cycle in its 'natural' state prior to interference by humans. In fact, the form of that 'natural' state depends entirely on what time period is considered. If the view were to be shifted back several hundred million years you would encounter a very different 'natural' state. For now, the time zone for 'natural' will be the last few thousand years before the influence of the Industrial Revolution (see Block 1, Table 2.3). The sizes of the reservoirs are much larger than the rates of movement. Indeed, you do not need to know the sizes of the reservoirs to understand the changes that occur over time. Imagine a large kitchen sink half full with water, with a leaky plug. If we turn the tap on, we can adjust the flow into the sink so that the level does not change. Suppose then that the rate of leakage through the outlet increases. We can still maintain the level at half full by adjusting the tap again and increasing the flow to match the leakage. The size of the kitchen sink is not relevant to the rates of inflow and outflow. The same ideas apply to rates of flow into different reservoirs in Figures 2.3 or 2.4. All you need to know are the amounts

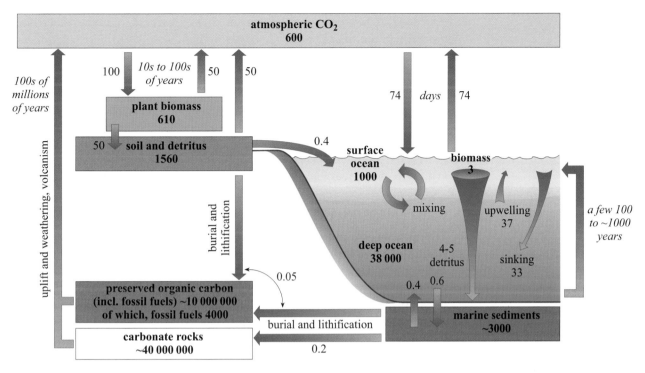

Figure 2.4 Summary of movement of carbon in the world prior to the Industrial Revolution. The units are in gigatonnes (10^9 tonnes, which equals 10^{12} kg)

entering or leaving the reservoir (the fact that the reservoir is full of gas rather than liquid makes no difference to the calculation). So, in the pre-industrial example (Figure 2.4), what are the flows of carbon in and out of the atmosphere? We will measure these flows in units of gigatonnes of carbon (GtC) as explained in the Study note: *making sense of large numbers*, in the introduction to this part.

In an average year prior to the Industrial Revolution, 100 GtC left the atmosphere and were taken up by land plants. Similarly 74 GtC entered the food webs of the ocean, 50 were transferred from land plants and animals to the soil, and the soil returned 50 to the atmosphere. At the same time 74 GtC were returned to the atmosphere from the oceans and 50 to the atmosphere from plants and animals by respiration. The overall change in the atmosphere can be summarised as the amount entering minus the amount leaving. From Figure 2.4, the number of gigatonnes of carbon entering = 50 + 50 + 74 = 174 per year, whilst the amount leaving = 100 + 74 = 174 per year (ignoring the amounts from volcanism which occur intermittently over very long periods of time). So the amounts entering and leaving are the same, just like our kitchen sink.

In other words, the pre-industrial scenario is one of no long-term change in the amount of carbon in the atmosphere. In the kitchen sink–tap–plughole analogy the amount of water in the sink stays the same because the amount entering from the tap is equal to the amount leaving via the plughole. From your work in Block 1 you will be aware that the amount of carbon entering the atmosphere has increased since the mid nineteenth century owing to a variety of factors, including the burning of fossil fuels. The net result is that the reservoir of carbon in the atmosphere is now increasing by about 3.4 GtC each year. (Note that this is equivalent to the increase of nearly 2 parts per million of carbon dioxide shown in the Keeling curve in Block 1.)

2.2   Quantifying the Amazonian contribution to the global carbon cycle

2.2.1   How much forest?

So how does Amazonia fit into the overall global picture? Table 2.1 sets the scene by contrasting the areas of different types of ecosystem in the world and the average biomass in each of those ecosystems. Biomass means the mass of biological material and refers here to the amount of living plant material, of which about 50% is carbon. (Biomass is generally measured as dry mass, that is, ignoring the variable amount of water that is present in living tissue, so 50% carbon is the proportion of carbon in the mass left after removing all the water from the plant material.) In other studies, the biomass of dead plant material, such as leaf litter, or the biomass of animals, might also be included. Notice the distinction between tropical wet forest and tropical dry forest. The latter is characterised by a large proportion of the trees losing their leaves in the dry season. Most of the forest in Amazonia and neighbouring areas falls into the first category. Thus, although there may be marked seasons, the dry seasons are not so dry as to lead to major leaf loss or to favour plants with that strategy.

Table 2.1 Global estimates of total area and biomass per hectare of different ecosystem types. Boreal forests occur in the North, e.g. Canada and Siberia

Ecosystem	Area (millions of hectares)	Average biomass (tonnes per hectare)	Total biomass from each different ecosystem type (millions of tonnes)
Tropical wet forest	1700	450	765000
Tropical dry forest	750	350	262500
Temperate evergreen forest	500	350	175000
Temperate deciduous forest	700	300	210000
Boreal coniferous forest	1200	200	240000
Temperate woodland and scrub	850	60	51000
Total woodland/forest	5700	285	1703500
Savannah	1500	40	6000

Source: Based on estimates in Whittaker (1975)

SAQ 2.1   Forest biomass

What does Table 2.1 tell us about the importance of tropical forest as a carbon store?

1   What is the area of tropical forest as a percentage of the total woodland/forest?

2   What is the biomass of tropical forest as a percentage of total woodland/forest?

3   Compare the two figures from your answers for Questions 1 and 2. What is the significance of your findings?

4   Why do you think the average biomass for savannah is much lower than for other ecosystems?

Since 1975, there have been some dramatic changes in, for example, the area of tropical rainforest and great improvements in the methods of data collection. Much of the latter is due to the use and interpretation of satellite imagery, known as *remote sensing*.

Box 2.1   Remote sensing of vegetation

Differences in the light reflection or absorption properties of different types of vegetation can be detected by a satellite. This can be used to map the total extent of forest cover and different types of vegetation and crops at a given moment and to track their changes over seasons or years. It can also be used to identify particular types of crop and to monitor their health from the state of their foliage, allowing damage from pests, drought or fire to be identified quickly. However, it is important to check that the satellite images being interpreted match accurately what is actually happening to the vegetation and crops. This checking of data on the ground against satellite data is referred to as *ground-truthing*. Satellite data has been used to estimate change in forest cover during the 1990s (Achard et al., 2002); see Table 2.2. You should be aware that this data, just like any other set of measurements, is prone to various errors. Whilst this does not undermine the overall result, it is important to be cautious in accepting data without understanding the measurement and sampling errors involved. You will appreciate this in Activity 2.3.

Table 2.2 Tropical forest cover in 1990 and 1997. The data was actually collected on slightly different dates and standardised to represent June 1990 and June 1997

	Central and South America	Africa	South-East Asia	Global
Area of tropical forest in 1990 (millions of hectares)	669	198	283	1150
Area of tropical forest in 1997 (millions of hectares)	653	193	270	1116
Change in area (millions of hectares)	−16	−5	−13	−34
Annual loss averaged over seven years (millions of hectares)	16/7 = 2.3	5/7 = 0.7	13/7 = 1.9	34/7 = 4.9

Source: Achard et al., 2002

You can now see that the total (global) tropical forest cover in 1990 was 1150 million hectares. The tropical forest estimate for 1975 in Table 2.1 is 2450 million hectares. Even allowing for the estimate in Table 2.1 having a high margin of error, the total tropical forest area was formerly much higher. Thus a rough estimate of the total tropical forest loss up to 1990 is (1700 + 750 − 1150) million hectares, which equals 1300 million hectares. In other words, about half of the tropical forest was lost between 1975 and 1990.

Since 1990 this has continued, although at a slower rate; you can see that the annual loss across all the tropical forest areas is 4.9 million hectares, with about half of that annual loss in Central and South America.

Activity 2.2   Unpicking the rates of deforestation

It is difficult to visualise rates of deforestation. Use one of the techniques suggested at the start of Part 2 (in the Study note: *making sense of large numbers*) to help communicate the significance of deforestation described in Table 2.2. Make use of the following information: the area of the UK (England, Scotland, Wales and Northern Ireland) is 24.3 million hectares, and that of Wales alone is 2.1 million hectares.

Discussion
One technique described is the striking comparison. You can compare the global area of tropical forest lost each year, 4.9 million hectares, with the area of the UK, which is 24.3 million hectares. So an area of about one-fifth of the UK is being lost each year. Using Wales as a comparator, you could point out that the area of forest lost in Central and South America alone each year (2.3 million hectares) is larger than the size of Wales.

Table 2.3 shows how different types of tropical forest changed from 1990 to 1997. The different forest types are defined in terms of the proportion of the area that has continuous cover of trees and the number of trees present. For example, both open and closed forests have more than 70% of continuous tree cover in the study area but differ in the number of trees. The closed forest has the highest density of trees. The mosaic forest type includes other ecosystems such as grassland and has less than 40% forest.

Table 2.3 Areas of different tropical forest types in 1990 and 1997 (million hectares)		
Forest type	1990	1997
Closed forest	944	908
Open forest	130	134
Fragmented forest	36	34
Plant/regrown	9	9
Mosaic	31	31
Total	1150	1116

Source: Achard et al., 2002

SAQ 2.2 Loss of forest types

Which of the types of tropical forest had the largest loss of area between 1990 and 1997? What do you think is the most useful way in which you can express this result?

From the point of view of the carbon cycle, it is not so much the changes in area of forest that matters, but change in biomass. Estimates of biomass over large areas have also benefited from new technologies in remote sensing and data analysis, combined with ground-truthing from samples in plots in different habitats. Using these techniques, the distribution of biomass over the Amazon basin has been estimated (Figure 2.5) based on remote-sensed vegetation distribution and estimates of biomass in sample plots (Saatchi et al., 2007). Biomass levels are highest in parts of Amazonia, where carbon content of the biomass ranges from 300 to 400 tonnes of *carbon* per hectare, well above the global average for tropical forests, which is closer to 200 tonnes of *carbon* per hectare.

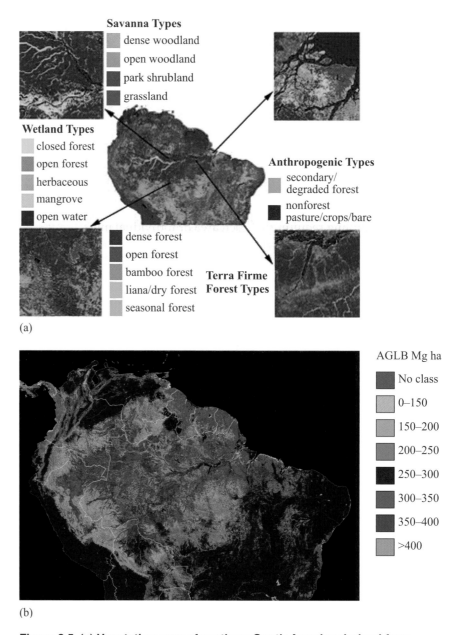

(a)

(b)

Figure 2.5 (a) Vegetation map of northern South America derived from remote-sensed data; (b) above-ground live biomass (AGLB) estimates for the different forest types. The 'no class' gaps within the Amazonia area represent other vegetation types, e.g. savannah. Mg is 10^6 g which is tonnes. *(Source: Saatchi et al., 2007)*

In Activity 2.3 you will carry out a practical investigation of a small sample of the Amazonian forest using remote-sensed data from a satellite. In this activity you will be contributing to a U116 database of the status and change in the abundance of different ecosystems and habitats, especially tropical forest, in Amazonia. This activity also builds on Activities 2.1 and 2.2, where you explored the extent of deforestation in the Amazon region.

Box 2.2   Sampling

When ecologists wish to investigate the abundance of plants or animals in populations, communities or ecosystems, it is usually impossible to make measurements on each plant or animal. There may simply be too many individuals or they are too widespread to physically measure. Instead, measurements are made on samples of individuals. There are statistical techniques that should be employed to decide on how samples are taken, the number of samples to be used, etc. to ensure that the sample is as unbiased and representative as possible.

Random sampling requires that each area or individual must have an equal chance of being chosen for each sample and must avoid any bias on the part of the researcher. In studying a large area of forest, for example, random positions may be chosen for measurements using numbers taken from a andom number table, which can be used to determine the coordinates of the sampling position.

There are instances where it is appropriate to select a systematic sampling procedure. If the whole area of the Amazon were to be randomly sampled then some habitats, e.g. scrub or agricultural land, might be missed. Stratified random sampling is a process of selecting a sample in such a way that identified subgroups in the population are represented. In Amazonia several different habitats, such as agricultural land and forest, may be selected and then sampled randomly within these habitats.

These techniques of sampling are not just the preserve of ecology. In surveying human populations, e.g. in opinion polls, a researcher may specifically seek to include participants of various minority groups, based on their proportionality to the total population. This kind of stratified random sampling could then claim to be more representative of the country's population than a simple random survey.

Activity 2.3   Assessing change in the Amazon

Go to the U116 course website, select Block 4, Web resources, and click on 'Assessing change in the Amazon'.

2.2.2   Using the information on biomass

The biomass of the forests provides a measure of part of the storage of carbon and other forest components.

In terms of carbon cycling, the processes of photosynthesis and respiration can be collected together into two boxes (Figure 2.6). The arrows in Figure 2.6 indicate the flow of carbon atoms. After capture by plants, the carbon can be lost by respiration (perhaps after being consumed by animals) or it can enter the vegetation and soil storage box. Eventually it will be released by respiration back into the atmosphere. So it can be seen that these three boxes and the arrows between them provide a convenient summary of the processes of carbon movement and storage in an area such as Amazonia. These areas can link to geographically distinct areas via the atmosphere. Here all the other carbon reservoirs are combined into one box. This includes other soil, terrestrial plant and animal (including humans), and freshwater and marine systems. One potentially important carbon flow between Amazonia and the rest of the world that is missing from Figure 2.6 is direct movement into the oceans, e.g. loss of carbon in silt via the river systems. For the time being the oceanic link will be ignored and you will concentrate on carbon exchange via the atmosphere.

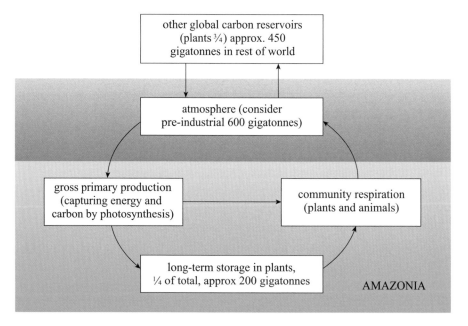

Figure 2.6 Carbon cycling in Amazonia and its relationship to the rest of the Earth

To provide an understanding of the effect of changes in the size and composition of Amazonian forest on the global carbon cycle, the quantities of carbon involved are needed.

The amount of carbon stored in the Amazon basin can be estimated by knowing the area of the catchment (7 million km^2 = 700 million hectares or 7×10^8 ha) and the average carbon content of the biomass (tonnes of carbon per hectare); the two values could be multiplied together to give total carbon storage. A major assumption here is that the abundance of each type of ecosystem in Amazonia is known. From Figure 2.5, approximately one-quarter of the area is covered with the highest biomass category (400–450 tonnes C per hectare). So the assumption we will use is that one-quarter has a biomass of 400 tonnes per hectare and that the remaining three-quarters has 200 tonnes per hectare. The amount of carbon stored in the Amazon basin can be estimated as follows:

For the area with the highest amount the biomass is:

$$0.25 \times (7 \times 10^8) \times 400 \text{ tonnes of carbon per hectare.}$$

For the remaining area the biomass is:

$$0.75 \times (7 \times 10^8) \times 200 \text{ tonnes of carbon per hectare.}$$

The total is:

$$(100 \times 7 \times 10^8) + (150 \times 7 \times 10^8)$$

$$= 700 \times 10^8 + 1050 \times 10^8$$

$$= 1750 \times 10^8 \text{ tonnes of carbon per hectare.}$$

This can be expressed in scientific notation as:

$$1.75 \times 10^3 \times 10^8 \text{ tonnes}$$

$$= 1.75 \times 10^{11} \text{ tonnes (175 gigatonnes) or } 1.75 \times 10^{14} \text{ kg.}$$

The world total reservoir of carbon in plants on land has been estimated to be 6.1×10^{14} kg (Figure 2.4; the amount stored in animals is relatively small). So the global vegetation estimate is about 3.5 times our estimate for Amazonia. Even allowing for the frailties of estimation it is clear that the above-ground biomass in Amazonia today will represent a major fraction of the world's carbon stored in plants and animals. The storage of carbon in all living organisms is referred to as the *biotic reservoir*. One-quarter of the world's biotic reservoir in Amazonia seems a reasonable estimate.

In Part 3 the question about the importance of Amazonia in global terms in the carbon cycle will be addressed.

Summary of Section 2

The importance of carbon to all life on Earth has been discussed and the carbon cycle was considered at different spatial scales, with the emphasis on the global cycle. Evaluation of the carbon cycle can be related to the flow of carbon between different reservoirs and the residence time within reservoirs. The loss of tropical forest was highlighted and compared across regions and time periods. Remote sensing has greatly improved the opportunities for monitoring and quantifying change in tropical forests and other environments.

3   Managing forests sustainably

3.1   Sustainability revisited

In Block 1 you saw how sustainability can be considered to be the product of social, economic and environmental factors. In Part 3 of this block you will discover the importance of the interplay between these factors, leading to an assessment of the possible futures for Amazonia. In this section the foundations of the environmental aspects of sustainability will be discussed.

In Block 1 a definition of sustainable development from the Brundtland report was introduced: 'development that meets the needs of the present without compromising the ability of future generations to meet their own needs.' (WCED, 1987).

How can this broad concept be applied to the environments of Amazonia? In one sense, it is quite straightforward. The requirement is that some of the forest or savannah can be used now (for whatever purpose) as long as enough of it is left for future use. But if the resource is finite, how much can people continue to use? Again, there is an apparently simple answer. If the resource, such as timber or medicines, is derived from plants then a certain fraction can be removed over a given time period, leaving the remainder to grow for use in the following time period (this is discussed in Part 3). The same argument can be applied to the harvesting of animals for food. As long as enough of the animal population is left, it will multiply so that it can be harvested again in the future. Clearly, the extent to which a plant or animal can be harvested or otherwise used so that sufficient remains for the future needs to be decided. However, this approach ignores the possible conflicts of interest or differences of opinion over how to do this. The studies of water use and conservation in Block 3 pointed clearly to the need to involve and get the agreement of all groups who might have an interest in using or protecting a forest or water source. This very difficult process is sometimes put to one side in the remainder of this section to focus more on the ecological aspects of land management. Another problem for sustainable development lies in the word 'development'. This suggests that growth or change needs to occur. Whilst this may be possible up to a point, there are obviously limits to sustainable utilisation of natural resources. Pushing the boundaries too far will result in reduction of the target organism towards extinction. So, it is not possible to envisage a continual growth in human population without it resulting in catastrophic effects on natural resources. For this reason, environmental scientists and economists have put considerable effort into determining the criteria for sustainable harvesting of plants and animals.

3.2   An ecological perspective on sustainability

Theories of managing resources sustainably have a long history. Early work on fisheries in the 1950s suggested simple models for optimum levels of harvesting, resulting in the idea of *maximum sustainable yield* (Figure 2.7). These studies focused on single species and attempted to demonstrate that certain levels of harvesting could be sustained as long as characteristics of the harvested population, such as growth rate and survival, were maintained at sufficient levels. Inevitably those models were difficult to reconcile with reality as populations did not behave in the expected manner. Migration and complex interactions with predators and prey meant that new models had to be generated. Furthermore, the control of harvesting levels is more easily met in a computer program than on a fishing fleet covering large areas of ocean! There is, for example, an issue of how the harvested population is taken. If only the largest fish are caught, as often happens, then the action of harvesting may be giving the processes of natural selection a push towards favouring smaller fish.

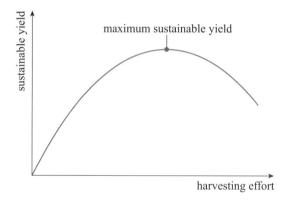

Figure 2.7 Single-species model of sustainable harvesting

In Part 4 of Block 2 there is a discussion of the role of Inuit traditional ecological knowledge and the nature of its relationship to scientific enquiry. One of the examples, a disagreement over the stewardship of wild Dall sheep, is worth a second look here because it gives a fresh perspective to this issue.

> But in discussions about regulating sheep hunting, members of the Kluane community expressed concern over the current practice of restricting hunters to shooting only full curl rams (these are fully mature rams eight years old or older). They argued that these animals are especially important to the overall sheep population because of their role as teachers; it is from these mature rams that younger rams learn proper mating behaviour as well as more general survival strategies. Thus, killing too many full curl rams has an impact on the population far in excess of the number of animals killed by hunters. One person likened it to killing off all the elders in their community.

As far as many members of the Kluane community were concerned, understanding the sheep's social structure and how the animals behave is every bit as important to them as the numbers sought by biologists. They had raised their concerns hoping to switch from a full curl rule to a quota system as a means to limit the sheep kill in the area. Both methods effectively limit the number of animals that can be killed, but a quota system would spread the kill more evenly over the entire sheep population, rather than focusing it on a particular age group.

(Block 2, Arctic approach, Part 4, Box 4.4)

The sudden collapse of cod fishing in the coastal waters of eastern Canada, once the largest cod fishery in the world, shows what can happen when resources are not managed sustainably (Figure 2.8). Twenty years after the collapse the cod population in the northern waters shows no sign of recovering and many ecologists studying this phenomenon place the blame for this on the lack of large, mature adults, which were selectively caught. The reasons for the lack of recovery are still not clear, but suggestions include the reduced size of mature adults, competition from other predators such as seals, birds and squid and other fish, and predation of cod eggs and larvae and young cod. While ecologists do not use quite the same reasoning as the Kluane community did, they agree with them on the importance of studying more about the relationships both within animal communities and with their environment.

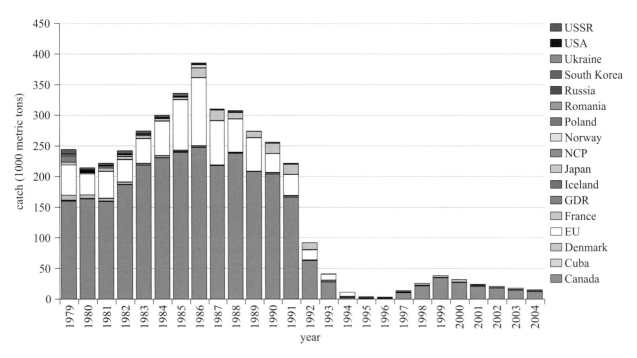

Figure 2.8 **The dramatic collapse of Atlantic cod stocks illustrates how quickly stocks disappear when an area's resources are overexploited** *(Source: adapted from NAFO, 2009)*

Terrestrial equivalents of the fisheries models have been combined with economic considerations and applied to high-profile organisms such as African elephants, which have been killed for ivory.

A parallel exercise was undertaken in forest management with the aim of allowing the removal of an appropriate amount of timber without damaging the ecosystem within which the trees were growing. Again, these practices are much more straightforward in plantation systems, where tree growth is easily monitored and the fate of other components of the ecosystem is a secondary consideration. Here the original woodland had been replaced, resulting in a considerable local loss of biodiversity. These practices, at least in valued areas of ancient woodland, are now being reversed. Instead, the focus in both temperate and tropical systems is on management of the naturally regenerating woodland. The sustainable management of natural forests, with the promise of long-term returns from timber and maintenance of the ecosystem biodiversity and function, is now a widely held goal and seen as a win–win scenario for conservation and economics. Yet, is this achievable?

Concerns about sustainability are not a new idea. An encouraging early form of forest management (sometimes classed as semi-natural management) was the *coppice cycle* practised in woodlands of western Europe over many hundreds of years. French peasants, for example, introduced formal management systems for coppice in the thirteenth and fourteenth centuries because they had an interest in maintaining the productivity of the forest. *'Tire et aire'* was a system of ensuring that the same volume of coppice was cut on rotation each year in perpetuity. Under this labour-intensive management regime, trees such as hazel (*Corylus avellana*) or sweet chestnut (*Castanea sativa*) were cut at fixed intervals (a typical hazel harvest cycle is once every 7–10 years), but not all in the same year. In any year, a compartment of about one eighth of the total area would be coppiced. The cutting left a *stool* from which the plants would regrow rapidly (Figure 2.9a) to provide poles and young wood (Figure 2.9b) that could be used for a variety of purposes from fencing to making baskets. Larger trees such as oaks were left for much longer intervals, after which they could be harvested as timber for major construction projects. In addition, parts of the forest would be used to allow domestic animals, such as pigs, to feed, while the seasonal hunting of wild animals also took place. Different compartments would be opened in subsequent years, resulting in a mosaic of patches of varying ages. These patches would support a range of woodland species.

Figure 2.9 (a) Coppice stool with regrowth; (b) heath fritillary *(Mellicta athalia)*; (c) coppiced alder

Today, large-scale coppice working is not economically or socially sustainable in the UK. People are less willing to work for relatively low wages in cold, damp and muddy conditions in the woods during winter, so it is rarely a socially attractive option. Markets for traditional coppice products disappeared during the first half of the twentieth century and are now very limited. (This was largely brought about by substitution of wire netting and barbed wire for hazel hurdles and fencing made from chestnut paling.) So, on the whole, coppice working is no longer economically sustainable on a commercial scale, although sweet chestnut coppice is still worked commercially in parts of Kent and Sussex.

However, the maintenance or reinstatement of coppicing has been a successful conservation tool. For example, in the UK the regionally rare butterflies pearl-bordered fritillary (*Boloria euphrosyne*) and heath fritillary (*Mellicta athalia*) thrive in coppiced areas, where their larval host plants (such as dog violet, *Viola canina*, and cow wheat, *Melampyrum pratense*) occur at high densities, i.e. high numbers per unit area. The heath fritillary (Figure 2.9b) is a notable conservation success story in the UK which has made the national headlines (*McCarthy*, 2007). An important ecological principle relevant to these studies is that high biological diversity is often associated with intermediate levels of disturbance. Coppiced areas that are too open or too closed tend to have a lower species diversity compared with areas in coppice mid-cycle.

Similar approaches have been undertaken in tropical forests, for example the Periodic Block System of management in some of the lowland forest in Trinidad. Although Trinidad is an island to the north of Amazonia, it shares many species in common with Amazonia as it is close to the mainland. The Periodic Block System involves blocks of 150–300 hectares in which only trees meeting certain ecological criteria are harvested over a two-year period. A set of environmentally sensitive practices are included, such as leaving large fruiting trees or those next to streams. After harvesting, the compartment is closed for 25–30 years. Studies of the component flora and fauna revealed that this management technique maintained higher population levels and higher richness of certain plant groups when compared with either plantations or continual cropping systems (Clubbe and Jhilmit, 2002). The total number of species associated with closed forest (the non-gap species in Table 2.4) was very similar in the primary forest and Periodic Block System. Total plant species richness in the Periodic Block System exceeded that of natural systems after 25 years (Table 2.4).

Table 2.4 Effect of the Periodic Block System on plant species in Trinidad compared with continual cropping and primary forest. Species were sampled in eight 100 m² plots. Non-gap species (which includes epiphyte species, numbers in brackets) are those characteristic of undisturbed forest

	Primary forest (no management)	Periodic Block System (later stages – after 25 years)	Continual cropping system (after 4 years)
Total non-gap species	123 (16)	121 (15)	111 (9)
Total gap species	14	27	55
Total species richness	137	148	166

Source: adapted from Clubbe and Jhilmit, 2002

To understand this further you need to appreciate what happens when a forest tree is cut down or falls naturally (recall the example of forest tree life cycle and light gaps in Part 1). The light gap that is produced allows the invasion of a whole set of new gap-colonising plant species. Seeds may be dropped by animals, or arrive on the wind, or seed may already be present in the soil, in the *seed bank*. After the gap is opened up there may be rapid growth of the new plants, leading to competition for space and light. As the competition for resources increases, so light and nutrients reduce at the forest floor and the opportunity for gap colonists declines. This influx of gap species explains why the early stage of the Periodic Block System has a higher number of species than the later. If one were to judge biodiversity on total species richness alone, then the managed forest would be rated the most successful. This is why it is important to consider the composition of the forest, since some valued species may be lost in the managed forest.

Epiphytes, which include some orchids and bromeliads, are plants that grow on other plants and are typical of undisturbed tropical forest (Figure 2.10(a)). They are often sensitive to subtle changes in the humidity and light conditions, so while a few of them are found in open conditions (even on telephone lines – presumably deposited via birds' feet), most of them are confined to the tropical forest. In contrast, many of the gap species (Figure 2.10(b)) are able to exist in a wide range of open habitats, such as along roadsides, and are less frequent in undisturbed forest. That is not to say that they are not natural components of forest – it is just that they are found at much higher abundances in managed areas than under natural conditions. Whilst tree fall is a natural phenomenon, and occasionally may occur in high numbers as a result of events such as hurricanes, it is generally a slow process initiated by older trees dying.

(a)   (b)

Figure 2.10 (a) A tree covered with epiphytes; (b) *Heliconia*, a gap species

The example in Trinidad is on a relatively small scale and works in part because it is tightly controlled. In larger operations in regions such as Amazonia, sustainable forestry may be more difficult.

There is now a substantial body of data demonstrating the effects of logging on different species and on biodiversity in general. Largely those studies are consistent in identifying particular groups of species most at risk, such as epiphytes.

Using these and similar data sets, authors have made recommendations concerning the control of logging to ensure that impacts on non-target species are minimal. Some of these recommendations are summarised below, based on Clubbe and Jhilmit (2002) and Meijaard and Sheil (2008):

• Improved legislation and law enforcement and increased accountability.

• The regulation of hunting in logged or recently logged areas where species are more vulnerable (e.g. more visible).

- Preservation of canopy and mid-canopy fruiting trees to benefit fruit-feeding species and maintain seedling recruitment.

- Better protection of interior forest conditions. For example, trails should be planned carefully and constructed in a way that minimises canopy damage.

- Leaving of dead or partially dead trees standing or intact on the ground.

- Prevention of streams from silting up.

- Maintenance of interior forest connectivity and connections between forest patches so that animals can move between them.

- Implementation of adequate recovery periods.

With reference to the last point, you have seen that the Periodic Block System in Trinidad recommends a 25–30 year cycle. These forests are dominated by a few tree species such as mora (*Mora excelsa*) so that the cutting cycle is (partly) tuned to the recovery rate of those species. However, not all tree species grow at the same rate, so if the cycle is too short the management system will start to shift the species composition in favour of the faster growing trees. Furthermore, there is evidence from Bolivia (Dauber et al., 2005) that the yield in the second and subsequent cutting cycles of 25 years may be less than a quarter of the potentially harvestable volume in the first cycle. This results in reductions of between 72 and 96% in economic returns compared with the first cycle. Losses of this magnitude mean that there may be large areas of Amazonia and other tropical regions where the exploitation of 'natural' forests is only economically viable as a one-off activity, with potentially detrimental effects on the forest ecosystem. Dauber et al. (2005) suggested using various methods to increase tree growth, focusing on fast-growing species with good regeneration. However, it is not clear what effects such treatments would have on other species.

An alternative to timber production in forests is to remove smaller components of the system. These may include products for minor construction, such as palm leaves for thatch, medicinal plants or products from animals, such as honey. These products, collectively referred to as non-timber forest products (NTFP), could also include animals (e.g. mammals, birds, fish, lizards) consumed for meat, although this is generally considered separately as bushmeat. However, the same principles of sustainable utilisation will apply to bushmeat and NTFP, as discussed in Block 3.

One clear difference between timber and non-timber utilisation of forests is the economic scale of activity. Whilst individuals may collect small numbers of palm leaves for making a basket, the large-scale production of timber requires heavy machinery and substantial forest areas for economic returns. Traditionally, communities have used timber for constructing their own houses or transport such as dugout canoes, but this would rarely have been undertaken (or, indeed, have been feasible) for larger economic return. A corollary of the financial costs and benefits between timber and non-timber products is that the former tend to be undertaken by major companies, whereas the latter are the domain of individuals, family or small community units. Acquisition of NTFPs may be for personal use or to support small-scale industries such as weaving or carving. Whilst this might suggest that NTFPs are likely to be a minor drain of the resources of forest systems, this is not necessarily the case. It is possible that a well-managed timber concession may have less long-term impact than a sustained period of collecting for NTFPs by a forest community. Fortunately, there are now a sufficient number of studies across the tropical forests of the world to allow us to determine the effect of NTFP utilisation. Examples of NTFP utilisation in two montane tropical forests in East Africa, Uzungwa Scarp Forest Reserve and the Bwindi Impenetrable National Park (discussed in Block 3), are shown in Table 2.5.

Table 2.5 Use of non-timber forest products in two montane tropical forests in East Africa

	Number of species used
Medicinal plants	57
Building poles	50
Wood fuel	35
Edible fruits and vegetables	21
Tool handles	9
Weaving and basketry	8
Thatch material	7

Source: Ndanyalasi et al., 2007

In Bwindi, the liana *Loeseneriella apocynoides* is harvested for basket weaving. Examples of liana species are shown in Figure 2.11. The liana was harvested in both protected and unprotected areas of the forest, with stem diameters larger than 1 cm significantly more abundant in the protected area. The densities of eight commonly harvested tree species, most of which were used as building poles, were approximately 2.4–4.5 times lower in disturbed versus undisturbed habitats across all sites in Uzungwa Scarp Forest Reserve. Ndanyalasi et al. (2007) concluded that levels of harvesting in both forests are higher than can be sustained, i.e. that continued use at those levels would lead to detrimental effects on the populations of plants themselves and potentially of the ecosystems within which they reside. A major difficulty is that setting levels of utilisation is seen as meddling by outsiders, whilst enforcement of harvesting levels would be unworkable.

(a)

(b)

Figure 2.11 Lianas: (a) base of a mature liana; (b) old piece of liana showing coiled section

Other studies of NTFP utilisation have considered the economic returns. Shone and Caviglia-Harris (2006) addressed the environmental economics of NTFPs in western Amazonia. Using a substantial data set and economic statistical analyses they showed that whilst agro-forestry practices that involved some deforestation and planting did result in higher diversity and value of products harvested, this did not translate into a higher income. In essence it seems that deforestation may be more profitable for most people. Certainly, there is far less reliance on the forest for livelihood now. For example, the opportunities for raising chickens or cattle are now much greater and provide a more reliable source of protein than bushmeat. Depressingly, Shone and Caviglia-Harris conclude that:

> Directing policy towards 'win–win' strategies may not be desirable for reducing both poverty and deforestation in this region since we find no clear evidence that these can successfully be addressed simultaneously.
>
> […]
>
> Sustainable development policy [should] focus on increasing the value of the forest, or reducing the opportunity cost of leaving standing forest on the household lot, if sustainable production strategies are to be more attractive to households in the future.

> *(Shone and Caviglia-Harris, 2006)*

A recent report from the World Wide Fund for Nature (WWF) agrees:

> The WWF report shows that the revenue currently received from economic activities in which the natural environment remains intact is not high enough to offset the non-sustainable activities, but finding mechanisms to secure global payments for the forest's ecological services would be a major impetus to both preserving the forest and paying for and providing for proper management.

> *(WWF, 2009)*

SAQ 2.3   Comparing methods of forestry management

1   Outline the main change in forestry management in its methods of harvesting timber as it moves to more sustainable practices.

2   List two main differences between non-timber use (NFTP) and using forests for timber.

3   Compare the coppice cycle methods practised in western Europe with NFTP today.

4   What advantage of the old coppice cycle method is used today by conservationists?

One important principle that emerges from these studies and the considerations of succession discussed in Part 1 is the spatial scale of study. Sustainability can be defined at different scales, from small plots of farmland to whole catchments and ultimately to the whole planet. What is sustainable at the household level may, as suggested above, not be in the best interests of the region or of the planet. In the next part, the issues of sustainability in Amazonia will be explored further, leading to the question of what the future holds for this region rich in resources and biodiversity.

Summary of Section 3

The concept of maximum sustainable yield was introduced. Ideas of sustainable harvesting can be applied to one or more populations in an ecosystem. Harvesting strategies in tropical forest were compared with those of temperate coppice systems. The duration between harvesting (cycle time) is critical for sustainability. These ideas can be applied to non-timber forest products as well as timber.

Summary of Part 2

The role of Amazonia in the global carbon cycle has been considered. Carbon cycles can be described in terms of the number and size of reservoirs and the flux of carbon between those reservoirs. Quantifying the sizes of reservoirs and fluxes between them is extremely challenging, with a reliance on remote sensing, ground sampling and mathematical models.

Use of tropical forests was discussed in relation to timber and non-timber products. Management systems that promote sustainable utilisation of forest have been described.

After completing Part 2 you should be able to:

- develop further knowledge of the carbon cycle at regional and global levels
- use web-based tools to assess and interpret ecosystems change
- explore the sustainability of different approaches to forest management.

Answers to SAQs

SAQ 2.1

1   The area of tropical forest is 43% of the total woodland/forest area. In Table 2.1 tropical forest is split into two ecosystems: tropical wet forest and tropical dry forest. Its area is thus 1700 plus 750 million hectares. This is in comparison to the total woodland and forest area, which is given as 5700 million hectares. This can be written in percentage form as $[(1700 + 750) / 5700] \times 100 = 42.98\%$, rounded up to 43%. (The units in a percentage, in this case millions of hectares, cancel each other out.)

2   A similar calculation can be performed to calculate the biomass percentage. $[(765\ 000 + 262\ 500) / 1\ 703\ 500] \times 100 = 60.32\%$, rounded down to 60%. In other words, the biomass in tropical forests represents 60% of the total woodland/forest biomass.

3   As a proportion, 60%, or well over half, of the total woodland/forest biomass is found in tropical forests, but their area is less than half, 40%, of the total area. This means that there has to be more biomass in a given area of tropical forest than in woods and forests generally. This is confirmed by the figures in Table 2.1 showing average biomass for each forest type.

4   Savannah is tropical grassland with a scattering of trees. Plant growth varies between wet and dry seasons, which restricts the amount of total biomass. Removal of tropical rainforest can result in the area being replaced by savannah with scant grass and small tree growth.

SAQ 2.2

Table 2.3 indicates that the largest loss of area occurs in closed forest type. Open forest has actually increased in area, possibly as a result of selective removal of trees from what was previously closed forest.

There are various ways of expressing the loss. The absolute loss of closed forest over the 7 years is 36 million hectares, which is one and a half times the total area of the UK. Expressed as an annual loss it is (36/7) million hectares, which equals 5.1 million hectares. Another possible measure is the percentage loss per year. This is approximately $(5.1 / 944) \times 100 = 0.54\%$ per year. This actually doesn't sound as impressive as one and a half times the UK in 7 years. Which is the most useful version is a matter of opinion.

SAQ 2.3

1   The focus of forestry management changes from harvesting a particular species, for example in a plantation, to managing naturally regenerating woodland or forest. The goal is to achieve long-term returns from timber while maintaining biodiversity and function.

2   With NTFP, plants are used for minor construction, e.g. poles and roofing, and medicine, with only occasional use of timber. Animals are also taken for meat or their products, e.g. honey. NFTP is usually based on small-scale activities by individuals and communities, in contrast to timber extraction.

3   The two methods are very similar, in that both methods rely on management by local populations and mainly use non-timber products. Under the coppice system trees are managed to produce poles for construction and fencing, rather than timber, wild animals are hunted for meat, and domestic animals feed in the forest.

4   High biodiversity is often associated with intermediate levels of disturbance to forests and the practice of coppice cycling (and the Periodic Block System) produces a mosaic of different habitats.

References

Achard, F., Eva, H.D., Stibig, H.-J., Mayaux, P., Gallego, J., Richards, T. and Malingreau, J.-P. (2002) 'Determination of deforestation rates of the world's humid tropical forests', *Science*, vol. 297, pp. 999–1002.

Clubbe, C. and Jhilmit, S. (2002) 'Integrating forestry and biodiversity conservation in tropical forests in Trinidad', in *Plant Conservation in the Tropics* (eds M. Maunder, C. Clubbe, C. Hankamer and M. Groves), London, The Royal Botanic Gardens, Kew.

Dauber, E., Fredericksen, T.S. and Pena-Claros, M. (2005) 'Sustainability of timber harvesting in Bolivian tropical forests', *Forest Ecology and Management*, vol. 214, pp. 294–304.

McCarthy, M. (2007) 'Heath fritillary returns as tree-cutting brings light back to the woods', *The Independent*, 2 June, http://www.independent.co.uk/environment/nature/heath-fritillary-returns-as-treecutting-brings-light-back-to-the-woods-454161.html (Accessed June 2009).

Meijaard, E. and Sheil, D. (2008) 'The persistence and conservation of Borneo's mammals in lowland rain forests managed for timber: observations, overviews and opportunities', *Ecological Research*, vol. 23, pp. 21–34.

NAFO, 2009, Northwest Atlantic Fisheries Organization, Canada, (http://www.nafo.int/about/frames/about.html (Accessed August 2009).

Ndanyalasi, H.J., Bitariho, R. and Dovie, D.B.K. (2007) 'Harvesting of non-timber forest products and implications for conservation in two montane forests of East Africa', *Biological Conservation*, vol. 134, pp. 242–50.

Saatchi, S.S., Houghton, R.A., Dos Santos Alvala, R.C., Soares, J.V. and Yu, Y. (2007) 'Distribution of aboveground live biomass in the Amazon Basin', *Global Change Biology*, vol. 13, pp. 816–37.

Shone, B.M. and Caviglia-Harris, J.L. (2006) 'Quantifying and comparing the value of non-timber forest products in the Amazon', *Ecological Economics*, vol. 58, pp. 249–67.

Whittaker, R.H. (1975) *Communities and Ecosystems*, London, Macmillan.

WCED (1987) *Our Common Future*, Oxford, Oxford University Press.

WWF (2009) 'Amazon could prosper thanks to emission payments, be lost without', 10 February 2009, http://bolivia.panda.org/index.cfm?uNewsID=156101 (Accessed July 2009).

Part 3
The future of Amazonia

Michael Gillman

Introduction

1

Part 1 introduced you to the incredible richness of Amazonia: its ecosystems, its biodiversity and some of its people. Part 2 concentrated on its forests, and ways to manage them more sustainably, and their importance for the global carbon cycle. Part 3, the final part, looks at the global interactions between people and the Amazon and asks whether the Amazon can survive in its present form. Can humanity coexist with the biodiversity of Amazonia or is it simply a matter of time before a large fraction of the species is lost? Traditional farming practices such as cassava growing are destructive on the small scale but can allow regeneration of the forest if overall human population numbers are small and migration of plants and animals from neighbouring undisturbed areas is possible. But what about larger-scale use of the forest?

The Amazon is not only rich in biodiversity, it is extremely useful and valuable to us and has been for many hundreds of years. Since the arrival of settlers from Europe the Amazon has been subject to a series of economic booms and busts as one valuable commodity after another is discovered and exploited, from rubber to medicines, timber and minerals. Each cycle of boom and bust has left its impact on the Amazonian forest and its people. In recent decades particularly, deforestation has increased dramatically as pressure to open up the land for agriculture has combined with logging to eat into the forest edges and make inroads into the interior. However, it is not easy to get a clear picture of what is going on in such a vast region as Amazonia. Information is often limited and not always reliable so it is difficult to describe accurately, for example, the true extent of the changes to the forest, its causes and potential solutions.

Part 3 discusses some parts of this complex story. It looks at the many valuable resources and services provided by the Amazon, including rubber and medicines, and major threats to the forest from agriculture trying to feed the world. The future of Amazonia is even more uncertain. The new pressures to its sustainability and ecosystem function, including those from climate change, are briefly discussed in the final section.

1.1 Ecosystem services

In Part 1 you were introduced to the concept of an ecosystem. Various ecosystems, such as those of mangroves and savannahs, were described. The common features of ecosystems are their ability to transfer energy from the Sun, via the food web, to different organisms and to cycle materials, such as carbon, through them. Ecosystems can be visualised as fundamental structures in the living world. Much attention has been focused on the persistence of ecosystems in the face of threats such as habitat destruction, pollution and climate change. In the early 1960s Rachel Carson popularised the concerns over pesticide infiltration into food webs through her book *Silent Spring*. Although the book was criticised at the time, more recent work showed how pesticides such as DDT could become concentrated through the food chain leading, for example, to the thinning of eggshells of predatory birds. This phenomenon is now known as bioaccumulation. (It was introduced in Part 3 of Block 2, which discussed how fire retardants came to be in the body fat of polar bears.) This and subsequent work has helped fuel the enthusiasm for organic farming in which the use of pesticides, herbicides and inorganic fertilisers is greatly reduced. Scientists and farmers have explored other ways of increasing yield and reducing damage to crops. More generally, there is a growing appreciation of the value of ecosystems to humans, referred to as ecosystem services.

Ecosystem services cover a wide variety of different processes. Consider a few examples. Mangroves help protect coastal areas from erosion. Woodlands near areas of crop may serve as refuges for pollinators (Figure 3.1). Mountain forests help stop landslides and increase local rainfall, leading to consistency of water supplies. Removal of parts of these ecosystems can seriously disrupt the services they provide. In many mountainous parts of South America (Figure 3.2) a combination of population pressure and increased building has led to the loss of forests on steep-sided slopes and the protection they used to provide from landslides. Landslides caused by deforestation may cause extreme loss of life and property. These events impact especially on poorer people, who are forced to clear land and build houses higher up the mountains. An example of this is seen around Caracas, the capital of Venezuela, where sprawling shanty towns (favelas) are being built increasingly further up the surrounding mountains.

Figure 3.1 Example of pollinator ecosystem service

Figure 3.2 Landslide caused by deforestation

Of course, forest removal may also lead to the loss of parts of the ecosystem valued for other reasons, such as endangered species. In Puerto Rico there has been large-scale building and construction in the last thirty years across the lower parts of the island. During the same period there has been a significant rise in the level of the cloud base as a result of a warmer and drier climate that is in part caused by the deforestation. In other words, the cloud is getting higher. One effect of this is that cloud forest, which depends for its existence on the moisture in the clouds, is also being lost. Not only is this cloud forest essential for capturing water from the clouds and cycling it to other parts of the island via streams and rivers, but it is also home to a range of endangered species and endemic species and is in itself a rare thing (Figure 3.3).

(a)

(b)

Figure 3.3 (a) Puerto Rico cloud forest; (b) endemic *Calisto* butterfly

The great variety and value of Amazonia to the world can be expressed in terms of its ecosystem services. The ecosystem services provided by Amazonian forests are listed in Table 3.1 under four broad headings: supporting services, regulating services, provisioning services and cultural services. Supporting services provide the global infrastructure for all ecosystems; without them there would be no ecosystems. Their impact on people is indirect or only noticed over the long term, but they are still vital to our survival. Regulating services are at first sight difficult to distinguish from supporting services. They describe how ecosystems regulate and maintain themselves and operate at the local or regional level; for example, climate regulation refers to the role of rainforests in cycling water and water vapour to maintain a humid and wet climate. Provisioning services refer to the resources that people take directly from the forests. In contrast, cultural services refer mostly to the non-material benefits of the forest, whether for tourism, recreation or simple appreciation. This includes the cultural and spiritual value it has for indigenous people for whom the forest is home.

Table 3.1 Ecosystem services provided by Amazonian forests

Supporting services	Regulating services	Provisioning services	Cultural services
Biodiversity	Climate regulation	Timber	Non-use values
Soils (including nutrient cycling)	Water services	Non-timber forest products	Recreation and ecotourism
Water	Nutrient retention		
	Carbon storage		
	Fire protection		
	Pollination		
	Disease regulation		

Source: Verweij et al., 2009

SAQ 3.1   Ecosystem services and the carbon cycle

1   Which ecosystem service has been discussed in Block 4 that illustrates the global role played by the Amazonian forests? Describe this role briefly.

2   Which other ecosystem services have been discussed in Block 4?

3   In Part 2 of Block 3 you were introduced to the idea of instrumental and non-instrumental values. Which of the ecosystem services of Table 3.1 falls under either of these two headings?

Summary of Section 1

This section has discussed the concept of ecosystem services and introduced the wide variety of services provided by the Amazonian forest under the headings of supporting services, regulating services, provisioning services and cultural services.

Feeding the world

2

2.1 The global food market and human requirements

With higher numbers of people, changes in culture, lifestyle and agricultural practices, globalisation and increased territoriality (including removal of traditional indigenous areas), the global demand for food for humans is perceived as one of the main threats to biodiversity. Maintaining secure food supplies without damaging biodiversity will demand a more thoughtful approach to food production and consumption (see Figure 3.4).

(a)   (b)   (c)

Figure 3.4 Some of the plants imported from and originating in South and Central America: (a) banana; (b) maize; (c) sugar cane

Activity 3.1   Food from the Amazon basin

You may remember that in Block 1, Part 1, Activity 1.5: *Where does your food come from?* you were asked to think about food items and their countries of origin and fill in a table. Look back at Table 1.2 in Block 1 and look around in your fridge and cupboards and in the supermarket next time you go. How many items do you think are from the Amazon basin?

Discussion

Countries included in the Amazon basin are Venezuela, Guyana, Colombia, Ecuador, Peru, Brazil and Bolivia. As with the Block 1 activity, you will probably find that it can be difficult to find out the true origins of food items. Fruits and vegetables frequently have their country of origin clearly stated, as indeed do Colombian coffee or Brazil nuts, but for other items their origins are difficult to trace. The course team came up with sugar, beef, blueberries, soya, avocados, chocolate, poultry, orange juice, bananas, guavas and mangoes as well as coffee and Brazil nuts. A small amount of research revealed that all these and other items were exported from Amazonia to all parts of the developed world. Add to that the large amount of soya that is exported (Brazil is the world's second largest producer (Verweij et al., 2009)) for animal feed, which is undetectable using the current labelling systems. Growing crops and raising animals inevitably uses land, which necessitates clearing of tropical forest, which results in habitat loss and the inevitable threat to biodiversity.

Activity 3.2   Farming

Watch the 'Farming' video, in which Seaford describes how he farms now. Make a comparison between how he farms now and how he used to farm. See if you can identify any advantages or disadvantages for Seaford and the environment.

Discussion

The advantages for Seaford now are that he can make more money for less work by growing eddoes instead of cassava. Also, he does not have to spend a long time fishing to catch fish to eat with the cassava, nor does his wife have to spend a whole day preparing the cassava. A measure of the success of eddoe farming is the fact that others in the community are following Seaford in growing eddoes instead of cassava.

The environment will (presumably) benefit from the decreased fishing.

The environment will be affected as the cassava would only grow in the hills and not in the lower, wetter areas where the eddoes are now grown.

2.2   Soya beans

Global demands for food mean that forest is being converted for agricultural use to feed people far beyond South America. Just as cassava is being grown across the tropics to feed an estimated 500+ million people, so other non-native crops have been introduced into South America to be grown and then exported across the world. Soya beans (*Glycine max*),

Figure 3.5, is a notable example of an introduced crop that is being grown across South America, raising major concerns over its effects, direct and indirect, on loss of forest habitat.

(a)

(b)

Figure 3.5 Soya beans growing in Amazonia

In 2006 Brazil was the second highest producer of soya beans in the world after the United States. Most of its production, about 70%, is for export, and Brazil is now the world's biggest exporter of soya beans and products (Verweij et al., 2009, p. 35). The total area covered was about 22 million hectares, and both the area under production and the output of soya beans have increased dramatically (Table 3.2), with 20% of the area in the Brazilian state of Mato Grosso (meaning 'thick brushwood') on the southern edge of the Amazon forest. The natural vegetation of the northern half of the state is forest, whilst the southern half is home to savannah (cerrado) and wetland (Pantanal).

Table 3.2 Soya bean area and production in Brazil						
	1990/91	**1995/96**	**1999/00**	**2002/03**	**2005/06**	**2007/08**
Production (million tonnes)	15.4	23.2	32.9	52.0	55.0	60.2
Area harvested (million hectares)	9.7	10.7	13.6	18.5	22.7	21.3

Source: CONAB, 2008

SAQ 3.2   Soya bean production

1   By how much, approximately, have soya bean area and production increased between 1990/91 and 2007/08?

2   What reasons can you give for this increase in production?

Soya beans are mainly used for feeding to animals which are then consumed by humans. About 80% of soya beans are used as animal feed, but they also appear in some two-thirds of all processed foods for human consumption. You might like to look briefly at any ready meals or similar products that you have in your house to see how widespread is the use of soya. While soya bean production has increased dramatically throughout Brazil since 1990 (Table 3.2), encouraged by a worldwide shortage of animal-feed protein, much of the increase since the turn of the century has occurred in states in the north and west of Brazil which either border, or are in, the Amazon biome. It has been encouraged there by two factors: the development of new varieties that tolerated the humid conditions of the north, and the lower cost of land in Amazonia. Production of soya beans in these Amazonian states more than doubled between 1999/00 and 2004/05, mostly taking place outside of the forest on cerrado land. Although the area of rainforest directly converted for soya bean cultivation is still comparatively small, about 1 million hectares, the need to export the produce has led to the creation of transport infrastructures (highways and a deep port in Santarém; see Figure 3.6) allowing easier access into the forest areas with subsequent illegal colonisation along roadsides and river banks. The EU has been a major consumer of soya bean for animal feed owing to restrictions on feeding animal-derived protein to cattle following the incidence of Bovine Spongiform Encephalopathy, a brain disease in cattle that may be transmissible to humans. China is also a major importer, driven by increasing middle-class affluence and selection of soya-fed pork and poultry, as will be discussed in Block 5.

Concerns over soya bean production in Amazonia led to a commitment by the Brazilian Vegetable Oils Industry Association (ABIOVE) and the National Grain Exporters Association (ANEC) not to trade soya produced in areas in the Amazon biome that were deforested after July 2006. The initial commitment was for two years, subsequently extended in 2008 for another year. A simultaneous downturn in the soya industry's economic fortunes reduced the demand for new plantations, but it is claimed that the reduction

Figure 3.6 Map of soya highways: (a) the route out of Mato Grosso to Santarém; (b) a major transport route out of Amazonia to join the Pan-American highway in Central America *(Source: Mountain High®)*

in the area planted with soya in Santarém was a clear result of the moratorium. In the Amazon state of Pará, 41% less land was used to plant soya after the moratorium came into effect. The Brazilian Amazon Soya Working Group (GTS) commissioned a company to take aerial photographs and visit newly deforested areas over 100 hectares in size in January and February 2008 to check on implementation. Within the 193 areas sampled, there were no reports of soya bean growing. Deforestation was observed to occur in areas near or adjoining current soya production, and this perhaps points to a limitation of the moratorium (ABIOVE, 2008). The minimum economically feasible area for growing soya beans is estimated to be 100 hectares, and it is claimed that many smaller landowners were forced off land in soya-growing areas to consolidate holdings into areas of this size (Caruso, 2005). Some, at least, of these dispossessed farmers may then have been tempted to fell adjacent areas of forest to establish new small farms. So while the moratorium may have removed the direct conversion of land for soya, it may still not have had as great an effect on deforestation as had been hoped.

A second controversial aspect of soya cultivation is the use of genetically modified (GM) cultivars. Weed control is essential to successful commercial

111

production of soya, but there are few useful *selective herbicides* that could be used on the crop. However, the agrochemical company Monsanto used genetic modification techniques to produce a variety of soya that was resistant to Monsanto's herbicide 'Roundup' (glyphosate). This herbicide destroys any actively growing green plant material except for the modified 'Roundup Ready' crop, providing very effective weed control in the crop. However, there have been widespread concerns over the safety of GM crops, and at the time of writing there was still a ban on the incorporation of GM soya into foods used for direct human consumption in Europe. This ban did not extend to animal feedstuffs. In addition, the very effectiveness of the herbicide may be having direct effects on biodiversity in areas where it is used extensively, since 'weed' species may be an important component of the local food web. Partly because of this concern, and partly because the climate is warm enough to allow valuable second crops, GM soya is hardly used in the Brazilian Amazon, though it is used elsewhere in the country. In contrast, Brazil's main competitors, the US and Argentina, produce mostly GM soya. Perversely, pressure to grow soya in the Amazonian states may have increased because of the demand from environmentalists in Europe for GM-free soya.

Soya cultivation could potentially make a major contribution to our global food needs if everybody derived their protein directly from soya beans. It has been estimated that one hectare of soya can potentially produce enough protein to supply the needs of approximately 50 people. A rough calculation suggests that 140 million hectares would be needed just to grow this protein. (If one hectare produces sufficient protein for 50 people then the global population of 7 billion people require 7 billion/50 = 140 million hectares). This compares with the 22 million hectares currently being farmed for soya bean in Brazil. The new area would represent about one-sixth of the area of Brazil, so assuming that this area was suitable for growing soya beans it is theoretically possible for Brazil to grow enough to feed the world. At the moment, most of the soya grown in Amazonia is supplied to animals to provide food for humans, which feeds far fewer of us. As you will see in Block 5, there are reasons why this is done. However, within Brazil there is also a strong link between the economics of growing soya beans and cattle farming, which is explored in the next section and illustrates the major stresses that can be imposed on areas such as Brazil (and therefore Amazonia) as a top producer of human food in a global economy.

2.3   Cattle ranching

The cultivation of soya beans is not the only cause of deforestation in the Brazilian Amazon: its land is also being used for a variety of commercial crops from palm oil to tropical fruit. Soya is not even the main cause of deforestation, which is due to cattle ranching for beef production. In this section we concentrate again on Brazil to study the impact of cattle ranching on Amazonia. Seven states from the northern region and parts of the central–west region of Brazil (including Amazonas, Pará and Mato Grosso – shown in the second figure in the article below) are known collectively as 'Legal Amazonia'. Four-fifths of this area is forest, one-fifth savannah (cerrado) and scrub, and together they make up about 60% of Brazil's total land.

According to the WWF (Verweij et al., 2009, p. 38), Brazil has the second largest herd of cattle in the world after India, and it is grown mostly for beef. Beef consumption in Brazil is very high, 40 kg per person per year and growing, but although Brazil only exports 8% of its beef, it is still the largest exporter of meat in the world by tonnage. Just as in the case of soya bean cultivation, only a small proportion (about one-eighth) of the Brazilian herd is farmed in Legal Amazonia, but there has been a general movement of cattle ranching from the south of the country to the north in recent decades. Between 1990 and 2005, for example, the herd size tripled. A feature of cattle ranching in Brazil and in most tropical areas is that the soil has a low fertility, leading to what is called extensive grazing: typically a hectare can support only a few cattle, so large areas are needed to provide pastureland. In addition, land taken from the forest loses fertility quickly unless expensive additives are used. This means that after only a year or two it becomes more profitable to grow soya beans on this land and for cattle ranchers to move on. Soya bean and cattle farming are linked together in Legal Amazonia.

The authors of the WWF report argue that there is a feedback cycle involving both soya bean and cattle farming that is the major cause of deforestation in the Brazilian Amazon. The argument is made in the following excerpt of the report. It contains quite a lot of factual and technical detail, so as you read through it look for the following points and make your own notes on them. Then attempt Activity 3.3.

Points to look for:

- any economic factors and government or state policies that might influence cattle ranching and soya farming in Amazonia
- the direct and indirect causes of deforestation
- the evidence of the relationship between soya bean farming and cattle ranches.

Soy and beef complex

Excerpt from Verweij et al., 2009

The soy and beef industry are closely connected. As soy production in Brazil grows and the pressure on suitable lands increases, soy producers, who generally have easy access to relatively cheap international credit, buy land from livestock farmers, creating the soy–beef–deforestation cycle [see figure]. Through this mechanism, ranchers are given the opportunity to capitalise and expand their businesses without relying on expensive domestic loans (Landers 2004). These ranchers move toward forested areas, facilitated by the presence of soy-related infrastructure (e.g. BR163 Highway) and, driven by the low land prices, clear much larger areas of forested land along these roads than the area originally occupied (Dros, 2004).

Expansion of livestock farming into the Amazon is mainly induced by soybean expansion. Livestock producers are displaced by soy farmers, who overtake and convert existing cattle ranches to soy fields. The majority of the expansion takes place in Cerrado areas. The soil in the Cerrado offers suitable conditions and high productivity for soybean crops. These conditions make soy crops easier to establish, less labour

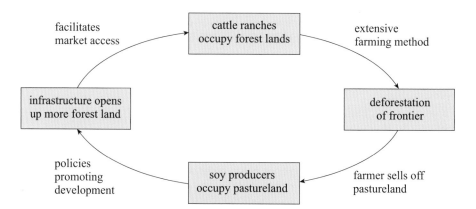

The soy–beef–deforestation interaction cycle

intensive and more profitable in terms of land preparation, given that most of the farms acquired are already converted to pastures.

The accessibility to transportation infrastructure is also a reason to prefer this area, because it represents an important reduction in costs of freight to export ports and crushing facilities. The 'push-effect', which soy farmers have on cattle ranchers, induces a shift which usually goes beyond the agricultural frontier extending into the Amazon biome. Once migration has occurred, the forest is cleared to re-establish the cattle enterprises. This cycle is repeated as the agricultural frontier moves north-east, threatening the Amazon rain forest. [The figure below] shows the movements of the frontiers. Two of the three frontier stretches converge in the south-east of the state of Pará: northern Mato Grosso and west Tocantins. The south east of Pará contains about 70% of the state's herd.

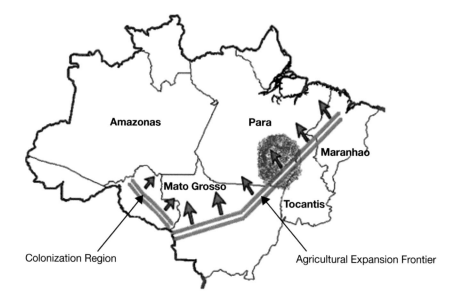

Agricultural expansion frontier and congregation of the largest cattle herd
(Source: Adapted from Cattaneo, 2002)

The Brazilian government calculated that the agricultural sector is responsible for deforesting nearly two million ha per year, mostly to establish new pastures for cattle ranching (USDA, 2004). The estimated area of pastures in the Amazon exceeds 24 million ha (IBGE, 1996) supporting 41.5 million head. The largest area of cultivated pasture is found in the state of Pará (5.8 million ha) and Tocantins (5.2 million ha).

Due to low soil fertility and unfavourable climate conditions, the Amazon land has a low carrying capacity, and should therefore be characterised as low productivity pasture. Calculations based on data obtained from the IBGE show that the overall cattle density in the northern region is of the order of 1.3 Animal Units (AU) per ha, which is similar to the average in Mato Grosso, but slightly higher than the density seen in the state of Pará (1.1 AU per ha). Taking into consideration the data on pasture extension from the last three agricultural censuses (1980, 1985 and 1995), cultivated pastures grew at a rate of 2.8% per year, whereas native pastures declined at a rate of 1.37%.

The soy–cattle nexus and deforestation

The soy–cattle complex is driven by federal government policies, designed to integrate the region within the Brazilian national economy (Hecht & Cockburn 1982). In 1990 Pará was the Brazilian state with the highest annual deforestation rate (4,890 km^2), closely followed by Mato Grosso. As a result of an intense, state-led campaign to promote agriculture development, Mato Grosso took the lead in 1992. Total deforestation peaked in 1995 with approximately 29,000 km^2, which coincided with a peak in beef prices. With a forest loss of 11,814 km^2, Mato Grosso contributed most to this overall number.

Agriculture expansion and cattle ranching have been identified as the main drivers of deforestation and forest degradation. Agriculture can be categorized as having a dual impact on deforestation: direct and indirect. Direct deforestation occurs when forested areas are directly converted into commercial crops such as sugar cane, oil palm, rubber, coffee, and tropical fruits, as well as cattle or other livestock. In contrast to popular belief, the main driver of direct deforestation in the Amazon is cattle ranching rather than soy cropping. Concentrations of deforestation coincide with areas of cattle herd expansion in agricultural frontier regions adjacent to or belonging to the Amazon biome. Indirect deforestation occurs when the expansion of soy cultivation results in displacement of cattle ranching into the Amazon biome. On the basis of an analysis of municipal data, we conclude that for each ha of newly planted soy, on average 1.15 ha of cattle ranching is opened up beyond the agricultural frontiers in the states of Mato Grosso, Pará, Maranhao and Tocantins. The figures for each state are presented in the table below. This results in conversion of (semi-)natural ecosystems in both the Cerrado and Amazon biomes. Not every hectare of soy planted will automatically translate into an additional hectare of cultivated pasture for cattle ranching as the expansion of cattle ranching is partly an independent process. However, Grieg-Gran et al. (2007) reported a multiplier effect for several regions, where the sale of land for soy production resulted in the purchase of a larger area of land for cattle ranching in the agricultural frontier.

Relation between expansion of soy and establishment of cattle pastures beyond the agricultural frontier. (Source: municipal data of IBGE; Agricultural census 1980, 1985, 1996; Pesquisa Agropecuaria Municipal 2005)		
State	**Planted soy (ha)**	**Cultivated pasture (ha)**
Pará	1	1.23
Maranhao	1	1.18
Mato Grosso	1	1.10
Tocantins	1	1.10

Expansion of sugar cane in the Cerrado is also expected to result in increased displacement of cattle ranching into the agricultural frontier zones, and therefore increased pressure on Amazon forests (WWF, 2008).

Pollution

The use of agrochemicals in large-scale soy production, mostly applied by aircraft spraying, leads to significant soil, air and water pollution. As chemicals are sometimes blown away by strong winds, the pollution effects are also felt by neighbouring farmlands, natural reserves, residential areas and water reservoirs (De Souza, 2004). Fish stocks are also affected by the indiscriminate use of herbicides, pesticides and fertilizers, as well as erosion, which influences the streams and rivers in which they live and breed. Soil erosion leads to increased sediment loads in the water, increasing its turbidity, which is also harmful to the fish.

Social impacts

Deforestation of the Amazon leads to socio-economic impacts at local and national levels. At the local level, deforestation forces many small producers to migrate to other areas. If they choose to migrate to urban areas, they often remain unemployed. If the farmers choose to settle in new, remote areas, another deforestation cycle is initiated. At the national level, agricultural expansion generates only limited welfare effects. In terms of rural income gain, increased production in the Amazon region replaces that from other regions. Thereby, any positive gain in a new agricultural area is offset by a negative impact on the other existing agricultural areas (Cattaneo, 2002). The trend whereby large-scale agriculture displaces smallholders is also leading to loss of employment at a national level: smallholder agriculture in Brazil generates one job per 8 ha of land (FAO/INCRA 2000), while industrial soy farming only generates one job per 200 ha (Carvalho, 1999).

References

Carvalho, R. (1999) *The Amazon towards the "Soybean Cycle"*, Friends of the Earth Amazonia, Sao Paulo.

Cattaneo, (2002) *Balancing agricultural development and deforestation in the Brazilian Amazon.* Research Report 129, International Food Policy Research Institute, Washington DC.

De Souza, M. De Conceição (2004) Sindicato de Trabalhadores Rurais Assentamento Sta. Teresina, in vídeoopnamenveldbezoek Funáguas / AIDEnvironment July 2004, Urucuí.

Dros, J. M. (2004) *Managing the Soy Boom: Two Scenarios of Soy Production in South America.* AIDEnvironment. Amsterdam.

FAO/INCRA 2000 in Galikin, M., *Partnership for a better future*, CEBRAC/ Rios vivos presentation at the seminar sustainable production of soy: A view on the future, Amsterdam, 2004.

Grieg-Gran, M., Haase, M., Kessler, J.J., Vermeulen, S. & Wakker, E. (2007) *The Dutch economic contribution to worldwide deforestation and forest degradation.* IIED, London, UK and AIDEnvironment, Amsterdam, the Netherlands.

Hecht, S. & Cockburn, A. (1982) *The faith of the forest: developers, defenders and destroyers of the Amazon,* HarperCollins, New York.

IBGE (Instituto Brasileiro de Geografiae Estatistica) http://www.ibge.gov.br WWF Brazil, 2008. Analysis of sugarcane agriculture industry expansion in Brazil. WWF, Agriculture and Environment Programme.

Activity 3.3   Cattle farming and deforestation

1 What economic and policy factors can lead to increased cattle farming in Legal Amazonia?

2 What is the difference between direct and indirect causes of deforestation?

3 What evidence is used to demonstrate the link between soya bean farming and cattle ranches?

4 Use your own words to describe the how the soy–cattle nexus causes deforestation.

Discussion

1   Economic factors leading to increased cattle farming in Legal Amazonia include cheaper land prices in the north, and the ability of cattle farmers to sell their land later to soy farmers, while state policies encourage the opening up of roads and other infrastructure to support soya bean exports, which then make it easier to access the forest and clear more land for cattle ranching.

2   Direct deforestation occurs when people clear new forest areas to grow crops or to provide pasture for cattle. Indirect deforestation occurs when soya bean farming displaces cattle, creating pressures and opportunities for cattle farmers to clear more forest.

3   The main evidence to support the link is the relationship shown in the table, showing that, on average, for each hectare of newly planted soya, 1.15 hectares of cattle ranching expands into new territory. This does not mean that it happens every time, but that there is a general relation between the two.

4   This is not always an easy argument to follow in the article, in part because it is making other points as well. It is best described in terms of the figure showing the soy–beef–deforestation cycle, which is presented as a continuous feedback cycle. Cattle ranchers clear and occupy land at the borders of the forest (legally or illegally), and because they use extensive grazing they use large amounts of land. Within a few years the new pasture land becomes low-yield, but the cattle farmers can sell it to soya bean farmers, who take over the land. The cattle farmers then move on to search for new land in the forest, helped by state policies supporting new roads for agriculture, which makes it easier for them to access new forest lands. With each cycle, more land is taken from the forest frontier. Jobs are only created or maintained as long as deforestation continues, but the long-term trend is for industrial farming to take over from smallholders, leading to less employment in agriculture.

Summary of Section 2

This section introduced the pressures on Amazonia caused by the global demand for food. It explored two commodities, soya and beef, where Brazil is a major global producer and exporter. The farming of soya beans and cattle ranching creates pressures to clear forest land for agriculture, through a combination of social and economic factors and policies to support agriculture. A moratorium on the trade of soya products from the Amazon states was introduced in 2006.

Renewable resource use from natural environments?

3

In Part 2, different approaches to harvesting forests sustainably were discussed. The principle is that removal of a small amount of natural resource such as timber, fruit or animals can occur without significantly affecting the ecosystem and the services it provides. This is possible if the plants can grow back or populations recover to previous, unharvested levels. This section considers some of the potentially renewable forest plant products.

3.1 Rubber industry

Many types of tree produce sticky sap that, when exposed to the air, undergoes changes in its properties to produce something that can be used by people. Such sap may also be used by butterflies and other organisms for feeding. The best known of the sap-producing trees is the Brazilian rubber tree (*Hevea brasiliensis*, Figure 3.7), but the use of sap from trees is not confined to rubber, or Amazonia. Balata is a substance taken from the sap of *Manilkara* trees that grow in various parts of Amazonia. The tree is also known as bulletwood, emphasising its strength and utility in construction, and the rubbery sap is used in the making of ornaments and toys. The following account is from Charles Waterton, visiting Guyana in the early nineteenth century:

Figure 3.7 Sap being collected from the rubber tree (*Hevea brasiliensis*)

> It is from this country that those beautiful paroquets, named Kessi-kessi, are procured. Here the crystal mountains are found; and here the three different species of the Ara (a genus of parrot) are seen in great abundance. Here, too, grows the tree from which the gum-elastic is got: it is large, and as tall as any in the forest. The wood has much the appearance of sycamore. The gum is contained in the bark. When that is cut through, it oozes out very freely. It is quite white and looks as rich as cream. It hardens almost immediately as it issues from the tree; so that it is very easy to collect a ball, by forming the juice into a globular shape as fast as it comes out. It becomes nearly black by being exposed to the air, and is real Indian rubber without undergoing any other treatment.

> *(Waterton, 1889)*

This appears to be a description of the Kanuku mountains, which were in view during Waterton's journey, though there is no evidence that he ever visited them. The tree from which the gum-elastic (balata) is taken, *Manilkara bidentata*, does grow in the Kanukus and has been harvested for many years using methods similar to that of rubber harvesting. The trees are harvested for several years and are then left to recover for about seven years before reharvesting. In the nineteenth century balata was originally used for making water containers and then by the British for golf balls. In 2000 there was a thriving 'cottage' industry of balata craftspeople at Nappi,

Cassava and rubber are members of the same family of flowering plants – the Euphorbiaceae

in the foothills of the Kanukus. Balata bleeding was a widespread activity in Guyana in the early to mid twentieth century and has been revived by some indigenous communities with an eye to possible tourist interest.

The use of sap from trees is a good example of a potentially renewable resource. Careful bleeding of trees may result in minimal damage to the plant and the conservation of large areas of forest. But can these industries survive and prosper in a global marketplace without compromising the forests? Like the examples of foods in Section 2, the shift from local to global creates an important challenge to sustainability.

The history of the rubber industry is a much grander affair than that of balata. The natural distribution of the genus *Hevea* from which rubber is derived is approximately that of Amazonia, with the most important species (*Hevea brasiliensis*) occurring south of the river Amazon. Most cultivated rubber plants were derived from *H. brasiliensis*. Indigenous people were aware of the properties of rubber at the time of arrival (and probably long before) of the first Spanish colonists. People on Haiti were recorded playing with balls made from a type of rubber in the sixteenth century. The first scientific collections of rubber were made by Humboldt and Bonpland in 1799 and 1800 in the upper Orinoco region (Lotschert and Beese, 1981).

For the next 80 years commercial production of rubber developed steadily in Amazonia. During the heyday of the rubber industry in South America it had a profound effect on the regional economy. The flamboyance of the Opera House in Manaus in the centre of Amazonia (Figure 3.8) is testament to the income derived from rubber during the late nineteenth and early twentieth centuries. The process of vulcanisation (invented by Charles Goodyear in the mid nineteenth century) improved the quality of rubber for use in tyres, and the flexible material had many other uses and became the plastic of its day.

Figure 3.8 Manaus Opera House

However, with the invention of the inflatable tyre, used first for carts and bicycles and later for motorised vehicles, rubber rapidly became a commodity of strategic importance for transport. World powers started to take an interest in its production. In 1877 about 70 000 seeds of *H. brasiliensis* were smuggled to England, where they were passed to the director of the Royal Botanic Gardens at Kew, Sir Joseph Hooker. The seeds were germinated and the young plants sent to the Botanic Gardens in Singapore to begin the rubber-growing plantations of Indonesia and Malaysia. Growing rubber trees in large plantations proved much more profitable than in the conditions in South America. By 1920 the invention of synthetic rubber and competition from the South-East Asian rubber plantations caused a slump in rubber prices and the end of Manaus's prosperity. In the 1970s and early 1980s production of rubber in Malaysia and Indonesia was about 2500 tons, compared with 30 tonnes or less in Brazil.

In the late twentieth century the rubber industry in Brazil continued to decline. In Acre in south-west Brazil, where tens of thousands of immigrants descended on the area in two waves (1870–1920 and the early 1940s) to exploit boom periods, the industry was effectively dead by the early 1990s (Salisbury and Schmink, 2007). Subsequently, rubber tappers have diversified into other activities, including the raising of cattle and pigs. A study conducted in the village of Triunfo demonstrated large changes in community income (Table 3.3).

Table 3.3 Community income sources from Triunfo in Acre, west Brazil. Values are percentage of community income. Note that cassava is sold here, so serves as both income and household food

Income source	1990	2000	2010 (projected)
Rubber	39	0	0
Annual plants (including cassava)	16	41	29
Cattle	4	5	15
Pigs	17	16	8

Source: Salisbury and Schmink, 2007

Activity 3.4   Impact on biodiversity

What do you think may be the implications of the changes shown in Table 3.3 for the area's biodiversity?

Discussion

The two enterprises that have increased most in their contribution to community income are annual plants, which would need to be replanted each year, with major soil disturbance each time, and cattle, which will graze on some form of grassland. While the grassland and cropland ecosystems may introduce niches for species that would not be found in the forest, these would not make up for the loss of species associated with removal of the closed canopy. Well-managed rubber plantations, on the other hand, would have much less impact, so their decline has increased the vulnerability of these areas of the forest.

3.2   Medicinal plants from the forest

Some of the most important products from forest plants are medicines, which have been used for traditional treatments but have also formed the basis of modern pharmaceutical products. In this section you will explore some medicinal plant products and find out how they may be discovered in unusual ways.

Activity 3.5   Medicinal plants from the forest

Local rural communities across the planet have been exploring their natural environment over thousands of years, resulting in the discovery of a huge number and variety of plants with medicinal properties. Watch the two short videos 'Medicinal plants' and 'The healing stone'; you will see some examples of the medicines from plants in Wakapoa as described by Vera and hear Seaford describing some local beliefs associated with a large stone.

1   How is local knowledge used to treat illnesses?

2   Why do you think that this knowledge may be lost in the future?

3   What role do you think the healing stone may play in the Arawak community?

Discussion

1   Medicinal plants include one that cures whooping cough, another that cures a variety of conditions, and another, the *buburo* plant, that cures malaria. This plant is poisonous and has to be used skilfully and with caution. Just enough has to be given so that the malaria parasite is killed but the patient is not poisoned. The medicines from plants are prepared with a variety of local plants from the local environment and are either swallowed or put on the body.

2   None of this information is written down, the indigenous language is becoming lost, and so the existence of the medicinal plant knowledge is being threatened.

3   The healing stone provides an important service to the community, as it is believed to confer bodily and spiritual healing. Beliefs such as this can be important to a community as they can encourage community and cultural adhesion.

How was the knowledge of medicinal plants first gained? Chance must have played a role in the origins of much early plant knowledge. Individuals happened to notice a new plant and possibly taste or consume it. They may have felt better (or worse!) and attributed those feelings of health or otherwise to consumption of the plant. It is also likely that there was some more systematic observation and testing involved. One possibility is that people observed the effects of plants on other animals, perhaps the effects on similar organisms such as primates. In Africa there are records of gorillas and chimpanzees eating hallucinogenic plants and undergoing frenzied behaviour, as though they were being chased. Once humans decided to try a leaf or chew a piece of bark, the taste would also be important. Plants containing medicinally useful compounds often have a bitter taste. A combination of information, such as avoidance or usage by herbivores, taste and smell, may have persuaded people to experiment with some crude extracts of all or part of the plant, for example incorporating the products into a bush tea (the combination of water and heat allowing the release of active ingredients). Indeed, early use of medicinal plants would have had much in common with early trials of food plants. Both of these activities required a close knowledge of the natural environment and have similarities with the applications of scientific method outlined in Block 2.

Activity 3.6 Environmental interpretation

Watch the 'Fish bones' video and make notes on the perceptions and interpretations of the natural environment by indigenous people. Compare these interpretations with those of a scientist. How does the fish bones story help with understanding the origins of medicinal plant use?

Discussion

The fish bones are, in fact, pieces of coral, possibly left there by earlier indigenous groups when the sea was much closer. Because the local people did not know this, and because the coral resembled large fish bones, they developed a story about how such a large fish came to be living (and died) in this area, so far from the sea. The story became embellished with social commentaries. The link to medicinal plant use is that the shapes of plant parts often suggest certain uses (this was known in Europe as the doctrine of signatures) which may have nothing to do with the potential medicinal properties of the plant. More generally, the story shows an awareness of the natural environment and a willingness to interpret it in ways that may differ from those of science.

3.3 From hunting to surgery: the case of curare

Protein sources for indigenous people were traditionally fish or bushmeat, with mammals such as labba (a large rodent) and bush cow (tapir) particular favourites. Iguana was also popular and easily caught. Today in many communities these are rarities and have been replaced by the ubiquitous chicken. However, fish is still popular and easy to obtain, especially in the dry season when water levels are low. Traditionally, hunting was undertaken with blowpipes and darts or bow and arrow, with different types of arrowhead for different prey. These hunting methods are discussed below, where they reveal a close association with the natural environment and a surprising outcome for medicine.

Figure 3.9 Indigenous person using a blowpipe

Preparation of the arrow poison commonly known as curare (urari), which is extracted from the bark of *Strychnos* and *Curarea* vines, and its delivery by blowpipe (Figure 3.9), is an excellent example of the ways in which indigenous people used the biodiversity of the forest. Forms of arrow poison were produced throughout Amazonia and used on blowpipe darts to kill a wide range of prey. The poison was also used to temporarily stun prey, allowing removal of, for example, a feather for a ceremonial head-dress. Although Europeans commented on it as a fearsome weapon, the blowpipe was rarely used to attack people.

The following is an account from Schomburgk:

> The complete hunting outfit consists of the generally 12 to 14 foot long blow-gun (Cura of the Macusis, Ihrua of the Paravilhanos), the quiver (Muyeh), arrows (Cungwa), the lower jaw of the voracious pirate-fish (*Pygocentrus niger*), the seed covering ('silk cotton') of the *Bombax globosum* and the fibres of *Bromelia karatas*. But of the whole apparatus the Macusis only finish the latter parts: they obtain the blowgun in barter from the Arecunas, Maiongkong and Guianaus. [The blowgun] can accurately and forcibly drive the arrow, over 12" in length, over a horizontal direction into an object more than 50 feet away. Small mammals and birds are the main quarry for this hunting weapon. The plant *Arundinaria schomburgkii* (the curata of the Macusis), which supplies the main ingredient of the blowgun, grows only in the country of the Guianaus and Maiongkong on the upper Parima and probably in the environs of the source of the Orinoco where my brother first discovered it.

> *(Schomburgk, 1840)*

Bancroft, in the eighteenth century, described the Demerara (now Guyana) Arawaks using blowpipes:

> Blowing these arrows (from a blowpipe) is the principal exercise of Indians from their childhood, and by long use and habitude they acquire a degree of dexterity and exactness at this exercise which is inimitable by a European and almost incredible.

> *(Bancroft, 1769)*

Curare and blowpipe were still in use in some places in Guyana in the early 1960s:

> The blowpipe was a simple straight hollow stem from which the pith had been removed by soaking in water. Two labba's teeth were fastened to it, about 18" from the mouthpiece. The darts (arrows) were about 10" long, with a small wad of cotton at the end. The points were coated with a dull blackish stain, curare, the notorious Indian poison, made from a Strychnos vine. A boy demonstrated hitting a mango about 40 feet away. Better than a gun because (e.g.) monkeys could be picked off one by one.

> *(Henfrey, 1964)*

Schomburgk reported that arrows for shooting are made from the midrib (central vein) of the leaf of *Maximiliana regia*, known as kokerite or coucerite palm, widely distributed in tropical South America (Schomburgk, 1840).

SAQ 3.3   Curare and biodiversity

What does the story of curare tell you about the way the indigenous people of Amazonia lived? How could this story be used as an argument for retaining the tropical rainforests?

Some examples of the composition of curare from Guyana are given in Table 3.4. Note both the range of ingredients and the scientific and local names. The *Strychnos* species contain the active ingredients.

Table 3.4 Curare composition from southern Guyana. Various other plants were added to the mixtures but only the main active ingredients are shown here		
Source	**Indigenous group and region**	***Strychnos* species (active ingredient)**
Schreber (1783) after Bancroft (1769)	Akawai, south/south-east	*Strychnos guianensis*
Reverend Youd and Robert Schomburgk, 1840s	Macushi, Pirara	bark of Urari (*Strychnos toxifera*) 2 lb bark of Arimaru (*Strychnos cogens*) ¼ lb Yakki (*Strychnos bredemeyeri*) ¼ lb
Appen, 1870s	Macushi, Kanukus	Urari-yeh (*Strychnos toxifera*) bark of Arimeru (*Strychnos cogens*) Yakki (*Strychnos schomburgkii*) same ratio as Pirara preparation

Source: Bisset, 1992

Strychnos toxifera (Figure 3.10) was widely recognised in various languages as the most important and potent of the *Strychnos* vines.

The purpose of all this detail is to make the point that a vast amount of indigenous knowledge was poured into the preparation and utilisation of curare-tipped darts, which gave their users a much improved control over their environment. European travellers were very keen to get the recipe for curare, especially once they began to discover that it had some intriguing medicinal properties.

In 1835–36 in the company of a Wapishiana who knew how to make the poison, Robert Schomburgk visited the Kanuku mountains to find the urari vine (Figure 3.11). This specimen only had fruit so he could not describe it (the flower is required for a complete description), but he recognised it as a new species of *Strychnos*, which he named as *S. toxifera*. The specimen is in the Royal Botanic Gardens at Kew. The curare maker refused to make the preparation for Schomburgk, but he finally saw curare being prepared in Pirara in 1839. The flowering *Strychnos toxifera* was found by Robert's brother, Richard. Later descriptions of Macushi curare preparation agree largely with that of both Youd and Schomburgk, in particular the primary importance of *S. toxifera*, the use of other *Strychnos* species and various binding/thickening species (Bisset, 1992). There are many reports of

Figure 3.10 *Strychnos toxifera*

additions such as teeth and livers of venomous snakes, which may have been attempts to 'improve' the effects of the poisons.

Figure 3.11 *Strychnos toxifera* **from the Kanukus**

Curare acts as a muscle relaxant. With a sufficiently small dose an animal may recover, whilst a larger dose kills it. Work on the physiological effects of curare was first reported by Benjamin Collins Brodie in 1812. Brodie also collaborated with Charles Waterton on experiments with a donkey in 1814. The donkey, administered with curare, appeared to expire within 10 minutes. However, Waterton managed to revive the animal by continuous inflation of the lungs with a bellows. The donkey went on to make a full recovery, implying that curare killed by paralysing the muscles used in breathing but that the effects were reversible.

In 1844 the French physiologist Claude Bernard (Figure 3.12) undertook some experiments on nerve muscle preparations from frogs. He showed that the effect of curare came about by the blocking of nerve impulse transmission to the muscles and stopping them from functioning. This helped confirm that the asphyxiation observed by Waterton was due to the paralysis of the ventilating muscles in the chest and abdomen.

Figure 3.12 Claude Bernard

In 1938 Richard Gill bridged the gap between the South American rainforest and the operating theatre. Gill was inspired to collect curare because he was suffering from paralysis. His doctor had told him of a mysterious arrow poison called curare which, although it was one of the most deadly poisons known, had occasionally been used in modern medicine because it had a powerful relaxing effect. Coincidentally, only a few months earlier, Gill had been in the forests of Ecuador watching, as he described it, 'the witchcraft-tinctured brewing of curare' (Gill, 1941).

Gill was able to bring back to the United States enough of the raw material (made from *Curarea*, a plant that is unrelated to *Strychnos* but produces similar effects) to allow the company E.R. Squibb and Sons in 1939 to produce the first pharmaceutical product from curare, Intocostrin (Figure 3.13). The first published record of the use of curare in clinical anaesthesia, using Intocostrin, was by the Canadian team of Griffith and Johnson in 1942. They reported on the successful use of curare extract to increase skeletal muscular relaxation in operations on 25 patients. In each case there was rapid and complete muscular relaxation, which developed within one minute after intravenous injection and gradually disappeared after 10–15 minutes. There were no serious side effects.

(a)

(b)

Figure 3.13 Intocostrin: (a) a poster advertising Intocostrin; (b) a photo of Richard Gill

Although modern muscle relaxants are synthetic, the structures are derived from natural molecules found within curare preparations. In the preface to Gill's account of curare in his 1941 book *White Water and Black Magic* he wrote:

> Primary credit for the discovery of this drug [curare], which is at once a deadly poison and a beneficent therapeutic agent of an importance hardly second to insulin, goes to the Indians of the Amazon Basin.

(Gill, 1941)

127

Therefore anyone who has had a surgical procedure that involved muscle relaxation owes a debt of gratitude to the indigenous peoples who discovered and developed this natural product. There is no record of indigenous communities ever receiving payment for this discovery. A selection of the variety of medicinal plant products with origins in North and South America is given in Table 3.5. The message for this part of the block is that medicinal plant products are a further way in which tropical forest can be valued, providing the possibility of sustainable harvesting and income from intellectual property rights.

Table 3.5 Sources of medicinal plant products from indigenous peoples in North and South America

Medicinal product	Plant species	Region of origin	Original users of plant
Muscle relaxant in surgery	Curare vine (*Curarea* species)	Ecuador	South American Indians
Anti-cancer agent	Ground hemlock (*Taxus canadensis*)	Eastern Canada	North American Indians
Anti-malarial agent	Quinine (*Cinchona* sp.)	Peru	South American Indians
Pain relief, possible hormonal regulation	Wild yam (*Dioscorea villosa*)	South and Central America	Mayan, Aztec

3.4   From toxin to medicine

The relief of pain was another important outcome from the medical arsenal of species. Consider the virtues of henbane, described by John Gerard in the seventeenth century (Table 3.6).

Table 3.6 'Vertues' of the three types of henbane described by Gerard

Type of henbane	'vertues'
henbane	Causeth drowsinesse, and mitigateth all kinde of paine …
	The root boiled with vinegre, and the same holden hot in the mouth, easeth the pain of the teeth
yellow henbane	Cure all cuts or hurts in the head …
	Doth stupefie or dull the sences, and cause three kind of giddiness that [henbane of Peru] doth
henbane of Peru	Remedie for the paine of head called the Megram or Migram …
	Mitigateth the paine of the gout …
	A remedy for the tooth-ache …
	Good against poison …
	Notable medicines are made hereof against the old and inveterate cough

Source: Gerard, 1636

Henbane of Peru turns out to be a very familiar plant; it is the tobacco plant or *Nicotiana tabacum*, originally, like curare, from South America. Ironically, the tobacco plant, which has been responsible for the deaths of many people, was originally revered for its wide range of medicinal virtues.

Why should certain plants have these medicinal properties? The reason why plants such as *Strychnos toxifera* and *Nicotiana tabacum* have such extraordinary effects on the body is the presence of a particular group of compounds called **alkaloids**. The detection and evaluation of these compounds is helped by comparative studies both within and between plant families. These comparative studies have often been facilitated by independent indigenous knowledge. **Nicotine**, an alkaloid in *Nicotiana*, is also found in some other members of the plant family Solanaceae (which also includes potatoes, tomatoes and the nightshades).

The key to understanding the action of nicotine and the alkaloids found in certain species of *Strychnos* lies in their similarity to **neurotransmitters**, which are compounds that either pass across gaps (synapses) between nerve cells (neurons), or across gaps between a neuron and muscle, the neuromuscular junction. Why should plant compounds that act as neurotransmitters have evolved when plants do not have a nervous system? There are two possible answers to this question. The first is that it simply reflects common metabolic or biosynthetic pathways between plants and animals. Because plants and animals have the same (distant) common ancestors they are expected to have some biochemical structures and processes in common. Of course, there are many major differences as well, but the structure and function may be sufficiently alike that certain molecules active in a plant may also be active in an animal. This can be explained by the fact that both plants and animals have a similar genetic code.

The medicinal properties of plants are due to particular *secondary compounds*, i.e., those that are not part of the fundamental (primary) metabolism of nutrition, growth and reproduction. Alkaloids are one example of secondary compounds. Not all plant groups contain the same secondary compounds and it seems likely that the compounds have evolved independently in different groups. There is also evidence that ecologically distinct groups of plants (e.g. long-lived versus short-lived) have different levels and types of secondary compound.

So, the second answer is that there have been selection pressures for plants to evolve secondary compounds for defence purposes. This includes defence against herbivores and certain fungi, bacteria or viruses. The evolutionary argument is that plants with secondary compounds will survive better and leave more offspring (which themselves survive better and leave more offspring) than plants without those compounds. Thus a plant with a compound that interferes with the action of a neurotransmitter in an insect herbivore might cause it to stop or reduce feeding. It carries its own insecticide. This argument requires that there are sufficient numbers of plant natural enemies to warrant the cost to the plant of synthesising secondary compounds.

Summary of Section 3

This section described how it is possible to harvest products from the forest on a renewable basis. The resources described are all from plants, including rubber (latex) and medicinal plant products. The history of discovery and utilisation of curare was described in detail to demonstrate the global value of the product. The mechanism of action of medicinal plants depends on their chemical composition.

Amazonian economics and biodiversity conservation

4

One view of the story of curare portrays indigenous people (and the region where they live) as economic losers in an intellectual property struggle which has benefited many millions of people outside Amazonia. To what extent is this typical of Amazonian resources? This question is a key one because the future of Amazonia depends, in part, on its value to the people who live there. An informative recent study shows that, unexpectedly, areas protected for conservation may be better for local economies than competing interests such as cattle ranching.

A study by Amend et al. (n.d.) gathered financial data from ten protected areas (Figure 3.14) around Manaus, in the centre of Amazonia, from 1992 to 2003.

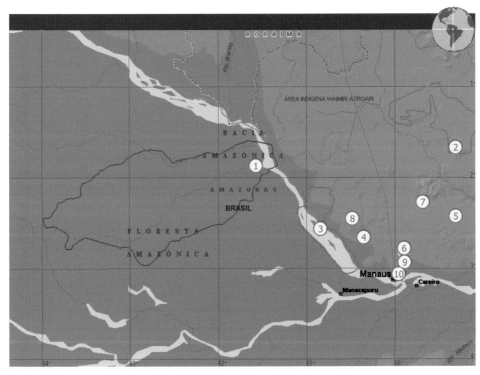

1. Jaú National Park (2,272,000 ha)
2. Uatumã Biological Reserve (943,000 ha)
3. Anavilhanas Ecological Station (350,018 ha)
4. Rio Negro State Park (157,807 ha)
5. Walter Egler Experimental Reserve (760 ha)
6. Adolfo Ducke Experimental Reserve (9,572 ha)
7. Projeto de Dinâmica Biológica de Fragmentos Florestais Reserve (2,488 ha)
8. Cuieras Experimental Reserve (18,900 ha)
9. INPA Botanical Garden (500 ha)
10. Mindu Municipal Park (33 ha)

0   50   100 km

Figure 3.14 Protected areas around Manaus used for study of local economics *(Source: Amend et al., n.d.)*

The study estimated that approximately 80% of income was generated from outside the state of Amazonas and more than 50% was internationally derived. Moreover, the average income per hectare competed well with the best returns for cattle ranching. Average income for local people associated with the protected areas was also three times higher than the average wage for Amazonia. The authors concluded that:

> Protected areas can be a strategy for local economic development. The strategy will be more economically competitive where opportunity costs are low and can be managed by allowing some small-scale economic activities. Local benefits are particularly large where the research activities are encouraged and where resources can be drawn in from government, private and non-governmental sources simultaneously.

(Amend et al., n.d.)

In this example they are optimistic about the role that protected areas can play in supporting both economic activity and livelihoods among local people, as well as the forests themselves. In contrast to the example of indigenous people and curare, local people and their environment do not have to become 'a sacrifice for the global good': the idea that forest protected areas only have a global value, for example through protecting global biodiversity or reducing atmospheric carbon dioxide. It should be possible for everyone to benefit.

You will see that there is a wide range in the size of protected areas, from 2.3 million hectares down to just 33. In total nearly 3.8 million hectares are protected in an area of about 23.4 million hectares (or 234 000 km^2), i.e. about 16% of the area is protected. This is just one part of a wider area network around Manaus, established by the Brazilian government in partnership with WWF (and other international and local NGOs) aimed at protecting as much of the forest as possible. By 2008 the project had succeeded in protecting about 25 million hectares in Amazonia (i.e. a little larger than the total area in Brazil used for soya bean cultivation), including the Tumucumaque Mountains National Park, one of the largest tropical forest protected areas in the world (Figure 3.15).

Activity 3.7   Protected areas in Amazonia

Notice the distinction between strict preservation areas and sustainable use reserves in Figure 3.15. What do you assume are the key features of these two types of reserve?

Discussion

A strict preservation area is one in which no human activity is allowed, in contrast to a sustainable use reserve, which allows some form of sustainable management such as selective timber removal.

Figure 3.15 Map showing location of Tumucumaque Mountains National Park
(Source: WWF, 2003)

Although the protected area example is encouraging, it is clear from the soya bean example that there is still a strong export pressure on Amazonia, despite the costs of transportation. In 2004, Brazil was the world's leading exporter of poultry, beef, oranges and sugar cane, predicted to be followed shortly by cotton, soya beans and biofuels (Nepstad et al., 2006). In the next section the various threads of this block will be brought together to explore possible Amazonian futures.

Summary of Section 4

In this short section we have touched briefly on the relative values of protected areas and commercial exploitation of forests.

5 Amazonian futures

5.1 The Amazonian tipping point

One way in which scientists have tried to convey the seriousness of global and regional environmental problems is through the concept of a ***tipping point***. This is a point at which the system under study tips into a different state, from which it cannot recover. To start with, let us try to unravel the fundamental processes that might lead to a tipping point (in general and in Amazonia) and then analyse the evidence from Amazonia to see whether it might be approaching such a situation.

To explore what processes might be involved, we will use a very simplified model to represent Amazonia. Imagine that it is covered with just two habitats – forest and grassland. Currently the area is dominated by forest, but grassland is increasing. What general and specific processes might tip Amazonia into a grassland-dominated region? Some of the specific processes have been discussed, such as logging and management of grassland by fire and grazing to provide the beef that is a major export. There are other less obvious specific processes, as you shall see later.

One important effect to consider is positive feedback. This idea was introduced in Block 2 to explain why Arctic ice was melting so rapidly. With positive feedback two processes reinforce each other, leading to rapid change (and not always 'positive' outcomes). In the case of Arctic ice, melting snow and ice interacted with rising global temperatures, leading to a faster loss of summer ice and a warmer planet.

In the case of Amazonia, the phenomenon of positive feedback can be clearly seen in the balance between grassland and forest. Grassland burns more easily than moist forest so the more grassland there is, the greater the likelihood of fire. But grassland is also less damaged by fire than is the forest, which in turn leads to the maintenance of grassland. Therefore, more grassland leads to more grassland! Under positive feedback the amount of grassland will continue to increase towards an end-point of pure grassland. Under natural conditions this extreme is not expected, although large historical fluctuations in the relative abundance of the two habitat types are known from pollen data (Figure 3.16). The amount of grassland is indicated by the abundance of grass pollen, whilst the amount of forest is indicated by the abundance of Moraceae pollen. The pollen levels of *Curatella americana* indicate savannah.

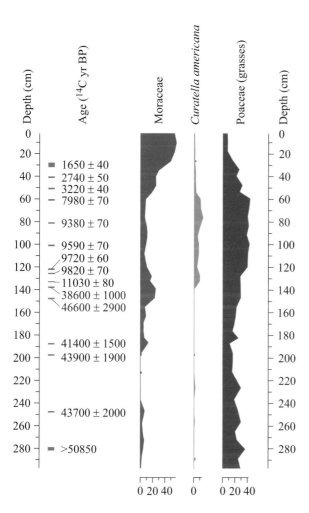

Figure 3.16 Long-term changes in the cover of forest and grassland in Amazonia shown by pollen cores. The method used is to sink cores through sediments and determine the relative abundance of different types of pollen. The amount of pollen is used as a measure of the abundance of that plant type at that time. The cores may also illustrate the incidence of fires by the presence of charcoal *(Source: adapted from Mayle et al., 2000, p. 2293)*

During cooler, drier periods grasslands dominate, whilst forests expand during wetter and warmer periods. In both cases some positive feedback is involved (grassland holds less moisture, leading to more locally dry conditions), but there must be some opposing processes. One such process may be akin to secondary succession (discussed in Part 1). Because they can grow much taller, trees can shade out the lower-growing grasses, so there is an inherent successional tendency for grasslands to develop into forest. If there is heavy grazing pressure, this can prevent or restrict tree growth, but if grazing is reduced for some reason, the trees can gain the upper hand. The interaction between these various opposing processes gives rise to the shifting balance between grassland and forest.

The suggestion is that, with the interventions by humans, these positive feedbacks are pushing the grassland state further (and faster) than it would go under the current natural climate conditions. It is also believed that future changes in climate may push Amazonia towards a grassland ecosystem through increased drought.

There are two major threats then to the survival of Amazon's forests: firstly, the direct effect from human interference to the forest and, secondly, the indirect threats from global climate change to the Amazonian region.

The Amazon forests have developed a strong resistance to the twin enemies of drought and fire, the mechanisms that push the balance between forest and grassland towards grassland. Forests that have survived for hundreds of thousands of years must have features that resist this change. Many larger trees in the forest have developed very deep roots, as much as ten metres down, through which they can continue to tap groundwater in the driest season to maintain photosynthesis (through transpiration) and keep their leaves intact. As long as the high leaf canopy of the forest is maintained, high humidity within the forest stops dead leaves and branches on the forest floor from drying out, even during the annual dry season. Fire is the enemy of these forests, but in normal circumstance this litter will not burn.

What are the circumstances that lead to loss or degradation of the forest? Major droughts occur occasionally. The last was in 1998 following a widespread disruption to global climate caused by a fluctuation in the Pacific Ocean known as *El Niño*. In the east of the Amazon it caused widespread fires and dieback of trees. The effect of the drought was made worse by slow-burning fires, many of which had spread from fires started to clear a patch of land that got out of control. They were able to get traction in those parts of the forest that had been degraded by selective logging, where up to half of the canopy may be lost, allowing the ground litter to dry out and become flammable. Thus human interference made a rare event worse, and fire continued the cycle of destruction by killing many more trees and setting in train the positive feedback cycle described earlier. Human interference is now causing this fire cycle to occur every year in the dry season; deforestation is not just due to clearance by logging. In the absence of fire the forest would normally recover rapidly.

The second threat to the forest comes from climate change (and it may already have started – some suspect that the strength of the 1998 El Niño is one sign of a warming planet). A climate model from the UK Meteorological Office's Hadley Centre (Cox et al., 2000) that included vegetation modelling in its calculations caused major alarm by suggesting that the climate of the Amazon would become so hot and dry by the end of the century that much of the forest would be replaced by savannah and scrub. This was one of many attempts to examine climate change in the Amazon, by providing a climate scenario for what might unfold in the future. Different models have not always agreed on this, but many support the idea that the Amazon forest, particularly in the east, will experience a significantly warmer and drier climate in future decades. More importantly, the threat from climate change is in addition to the current threats to the forest that have already caused deforestation. This is a general feature of climate change: the specific threats to societies or ecosystems from climate change simply add to existing environmental and social pressures and often make them worse.

Box 3.1   Scenarios and projections

Predictions about the future are rarely accurate, particularly when they are made about the direction that societies might take, or the rate at which economies grow. This is because societies are very complex systems, with many competing factors and influences. When scientists try to model such systems they use two terms in a particular way to describe this uncertainty. A *projection* is a prediction of future change based on current information and trends. It is uncertain because it involves assumptions about social or technological change that may not happen, or mechanisms that are not completely understood and may behave differently. A projection is often presented as a range of outcomes rather than a single one, for example that the economy might grow by between 2% and 5%. A *scenario* is a summary of a projected set of actions and describes both the assumptions and the outcomes. Scenarios are widely used by organisations to test policies or strategies by seeing how future events might develop under different conditions. They help to answer the question, 'What would happen if we followed this path?' The scenarios for the Amazon serve as a warning of what might happen if we do nothing to stop climate change and nothing to prevent deforestation. If we act differently, then the scenarios can change.

5.2   Nature in balance?

In the last section the idea of positive feedback was discussed as a way in which Amazonia might tip (irreversibly) into a different ecosystem (principally grassland). So what happened to the idea that nature is in balance? What processes might help maintain a mix of forest and grassland?

The harmony of nature is a well-established idea. It is a romantic interpretation of a natural garden in which there is space for all creatures and they coexist in perpetuity. In the nineteenth century the romanticists would have been dismayed by the notion of 'nature red in tooth and claw', which emphasised the predatory disposition of many species. The balance of nature was revisited by ecologists in the twentieth century, who pointed out that such stability was not necessarily the norm and that populations or ecosystems might naturally undergo large-scale fluctuations. Indeed, over longer periods of time, extinction was the norm and a stable climax state the exception.

Although ecologists discovered large changes in natural systems over time, they also realised that there were many examples of the stabilising effects of *negative* feedback. Let us consider its application to human populations. The mechanisms controlling human population increase (Figure 3.17) were considered by Pearl and Reed (1920) with respect to the United States, where high levels of immigration contributed to the increase:

> In a new and thinly populated country the population already existing there, being impressed with the apparently boundless opportunities, tends to reproduce freely, to urge friends to come from older countries and by the example of their well-being, actual or potential, to induce strangers to immigrate. As the population becomes more dense and passes into a phase where the still unutilized potentialities of subsistence, measured in terms of population, are measurably smaller than those which have already been utilized, all of these forces tending to increase the population will become reduced.

(Pearl and Reed, 1920, p. 287)

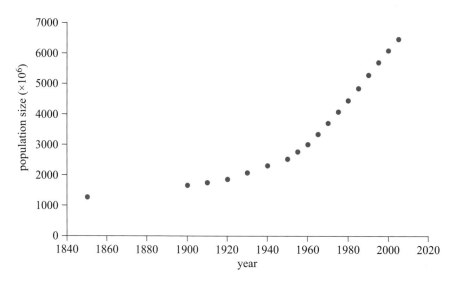

Figure 3.17 Change in global human population size from the mid 19th to the early 21st century

Figure 3.18 begins to represent Pearl and Reed's description as a multiple cause diagram. The 'boundless opportunities' are represented as the resource base, which affects the well-being of the local population. This in turn affects their reproductive rate, which of course affects the size of the local population. Similarly, the size of the resource base affects immigration, since the more resources are seen to be there, the more people will want to move in, again affecting the size of the local population. If you consider each of the effects in turn, you will see that in each case, as the item at the tail of the arrow increases, it makes the item at the head of the arrow also increase. This would allow the unchecked growth represented in the early part of Figure 3.17.

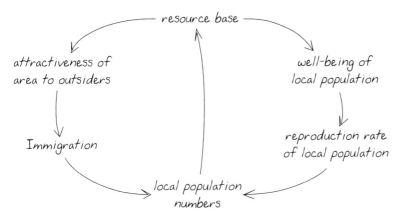

Figure 3.18 Multiple cause diagram of the situation described by Pearl and Reed

SAQ 3.4   Multiple cause diagrams and feedback

Figure 3.18 also has an arrow leading back from size of local population to the resource base. Explain what this arrow represents, and what effect the causal relationship represented will have on population growth.

Multiple cause diagrams like Figure 3.18 are useful as a way of looking for these sorts of feedback interaction. In Figure 3.19 this same diagramming method is applied to the Amazon ecosystem (using an example adapted

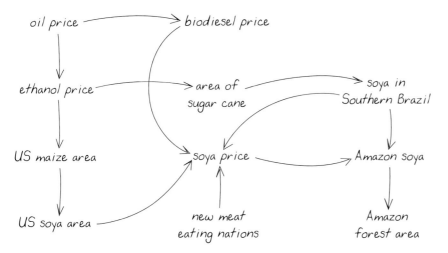

Figure 3.19 Multiple cause diagram of effects on Amazon forest ecosystem

from Nepstad et al., 2008). You can trace the potential effects of one activity on the forest ecosystem (Amazon forest area) by following the phrases and arrows from any one starting point. For example, increase in meat-eating nations (and therefore more meat eating) leads to an increase in soya price, which leads to an increase in Amazon soya production, which leads to a decrease in Amazon forest area. In this representation there do not appear to be any compensating negative feedback loops, suggesting that there is no current restriction, other than total cultivable area, on the conversion of forest to soya.

5.3   What future for Amazonia?

The one thing we know about the Amazonian region and its forests is that they are changing rapidly. This is due largely to human pressures, including large-scale deforestation described in this block. The destruction of this forest is of global significance for three main reasons. Firstly, the Amazon still contains the last great area of surviving tropical forest with its abundance of biodiversity. Secondly, the forest provides ecosystem services on a global scale through its role in the carbon cycle – if this carbon was released into the atmosphere climate change would be speeded up and an important sink for carbon would be lost. Thirdly, it would signal that we humans are incapable of living on the planet without causing serious damage to our life-support systems.

But there are many things we still do not know about the Amazon. Section 5 has looked briefly at some of the interactions between people and ecosystems that could have a bearing on Amazonia's future. There are undoubtedly many other factors and trends we have yet to discover. However, this does not mean that we should be rendered helpless by uncertainties. Scenarios can help us to decide what paths or actions to take by showing what is *likely* to happen given certain assumptions. Also, there are many groups of people and many initiatives and trends that are working to maintain the integrity of Amazonia's forests, or at least to limit the harm done. Nepstad, an academic researcher of Amazonia's forests, has outlined five trends that have

> the potential to prevent or, at least, postpone a large-scale forest dieback and provide some elements of a comprehensive Amazon conservation strategy.
>
> *(Nepstad et al., 2008)*

They are:

1   A growing tendency for landowners to avoid fire as a management tool because it might threaten their investments in orchards, plantations and improved pasture.

2   A change in landowners' attitudes towards more sustainable management practices driven by new environmental legislation, pressure from NGOs and others, and economic benefits of sustainable certification.

3 The possibility of restricting the advance of cattle ranching through legislation prohibiting clearing land that is marginally suited to agriculture (one-quarter of cleared forest land is now effectively abandoned, most of which is degraded pastureland used for a short time by cattle ranchers).

4 Creating parks and reserves or other protected areas in the path of the expanding agricultural frontier to form a barrier (see Section 4).

5 Using the United Nations Framework Convention on Climate Change (UNFCCC) to pay tropical nations to reduce their greenhouse gas emissions by preventing deforestation, effectively asking rich nations to pay poorer ones to keep their forests healthy.

These five trends include different groups of peoples (stakeholders) and a range of incentives or legislation. What they have in common is the attempt to place a practical value on the forest that would favour its preservation rather than its destruction.

We do not know what the future of Amazonia holds, but we do expect its situation to change rapidly, and we hope to understand much more about it. For this reason the concluding activity for Block 4, Activity 3.8, which is accessed from the course website, will be updated regularly to take into account changing circumstances. Its purpose is to get you to think about one aspect affecting the future of Amazonia, which might be the views or actions of some of its people, or an investigation of a particular scenario. The activity will also prepare you for the assignment associated with Block 4.

Activity 3.8   The future of Amazonia

Go to the U116 course website, select Block 4, Web resources, and click on 'The future of Amazonia'.

Summary of Section 5

This section introduced the concept of a tipping point to explain the risk that much of the Amazonian forest could become grassland from the combined threats of deforestation, fire and global climate change. However, there are many conflicting pressures on the Amazonian forest and their effects are often not fully understood – diagramming techniques can be useful to represent some of this complexity. The future of the Amazon is uncertain, but of importance to us all.

Summary of Part 3

The future of Amazonian forest depends on the extent, intensity and type of use of the forest. The role of potentially renewable resources and uses such as rubber and medicinal plants has been contrasted with competing land uses such as cattle ranching and soya bean cultivation. The continued existence of Amazonian forest depends on its value in terms of resources and ecosystem services, the economics of which are complex but may favour protection. The challenge of conservation in Amazonia is highlighted by the tipping point analogy in which reduction of the forest area beyond a certain point pushes it irrevocably towards a new agro-grassland (or at least, non-forest) ecosystem.

After completing Part 3 you should be able to:

• appreciate the importance of ecosystem services

• understand the pressures on Amazonia as a supplier of global resources

• recognise that different individuals and groups place different values on resources

• understand the effect that global demand for resources use has on Amazonian biodiversity and local human communities

• appreciate the role that sustainable futures play in the future of Amazonian ecosystems.

Amazonia plays a pivotal role in the global environment. It is home to a vast array of biological diversity and is a vital component of the global carbon cycle. Much of the biological interest of Amazonia is due to its long history of geographical isolation. Amazonia incorporates examples of several types of ecosystem, including tropical forest, savannah and aquatic. Despite its enormous area, the composition and function of these ecosystems are threatened by a wide range of human activities, driven by economic pressures both within and outside the region. The future of Amazonia depends on the extent to which humans value the resources and services of the region. Indigenous peoples have long valued the forest environment and been dependent on it for food, shelter and medicine. Some of their discoveries have benefited people far beyond Amazonia (and in ways they never imagined). A sufficiently high value combined with sustainable management practices may allow the forests of Amazonia to survive. The effects of climate change, some of which is driven by humans, may prove a sterner test.

Answers to SAQs

SAQ 3.1

1   Part 2 discussed the global role of carbon storage in the forest, its role in the global carbon cycle and its interaction with global climate change.

   The forests of Amazonia hold a significant part of the world's biomass. By doing this they can and do play a part in regulating the level of carbon dioxide in the atmosphere. In particular, destruction of the forest releases carbon dioxide to the atmosphere and reduces its capacity to store any further carbon as biomass.

   Note that the climate regulation in the table refers to the regional climate of the forest, not global climate.

2   Part 1 discussed the role of the forest in providing supporting services: biodiversity, soils and water, and pollination. In addition to carbon storage, Part 2 discussed both provisioning services: timber and non-timber forest products. In this section, the regulating services of climate regulation and water services have been briefly mentioned.

3   Block 3, Part 2 discussed the difference between instrumental values and non-instrumental values. An instrumental value is anything which has a practical use. A non-instrumental value has no practical value, but is valued for itself because, for example, it is thought to be beautiful. In other words, it is the same as the category 'non-use values'. All the other categories in Table 3.1 can be classified as instrumental values (even recreation and tourism, which bring employment and money to the providers).

SAQ 3.2

1   Soya bean production has increased from 15.4 to 60.2 tonnes, that is, by approximately four times (60/15). The area harvested has increased from 9.7 to 21.3 million hectares, that is, by approximately two times (20/10).

   If production has increased by four and area cultivated by two, then the yield has increased by a factor of two (production/area = 4/2).

2   The reason given in the preceding passage is the global demand for food. You might have thought of other, related points: increased demand for animal feed, increased prices, its value as a cash crop for farmers, and introduction of new varieties leading to better yields. Some of these issues are discussed in the next sections.

SAQ 3.3

The story of curare illustrates an intimate knowledge and use of the biodiversity of the forest by the indigenous people. It also indicates a degree of cooperation between tribes as they bartered their blowgun and poison components.

The removal of the tropical rainforests can unwittingly result in valuable and, as yet, unexploited plant species becoming extinct. The communities of the remaining indigenous people are also destroyed along with their long-held knowledge.

SAQ 3.4

This arrow represents the effect of population size on the resource base. In this case, size of population reduces the resource base, which introduces an element of negative feedback into the situation. So, as population grows, this will reduce the resource base, which will reduce the well-being of the local population, so this will reduce the rates of reproduction and immigration, so reducing population growth. This is the situation that is beginning to occur after 1980 in Figure 3.17.

References

ABIOVE (n.d.) *Sustainability: Soy Moratorium,* Brazilian Association of Vegetable Oil Industries, http://www.abiove.com.br/english/ss_moratoria_us.html (Accessed 1 June 2009).

ABIOVE (2008) *Soy Moratorium: Advances and Next Steps,* Brazilian Association of Vegetable Oil Industries, Report presented by the GTS working group to Mr Carlos Minc Baumfeld, Minister of Environment, http://www.abiove.com.br/english/sustent/ms_relatorio_ministro_7out08_us.pdf (Accessed 27 August 2009).

Amend, M., Gascon, C., Reid, J. and da Silva, J.M.C. (n.d.) *Parks Produce Local Economic Benefits in Amazonia,* http://revistavirtual.redesma.org/vol2/pdf/parks_csf.pdf (Accessed June 2009).

Bancroft, E. (1769) *An Essay on the Natural History of Guiana in South America,* printed for T. Becket and P.A. de Hondt, London.

Bisset, N.G. (1992) 'War and hunting poisons of the New World. Part 1: Notes on the early history of curare', *Journal of Ethnopharmacology,* vol. 36, pp. 1–26.

Caruso, E. (2005) *Roads of Deforestation in Brazil: How soya and cattle are destroying the Amazon with the help of IF,* WRM Bulletin No. 93, http://www.wrm.org.uy/bulletin/93/Brazil.html, (Accessed 27 August 2009).

CONAB (2008) Companhia Nacional de Abasteciamo, http://www.conab.gov.br (in Portuguese), cited in Verweij, 2009 (Accessed 7 July 2009).

Cox, P.M., Betts, R.A., Jones, C.D., Spall, S.A. and Totterdell, I.J. (2000) 'Acceleration of global warming due to carbon cycle feedbacks in a coupled climate model', *Nature,* vol. 408, pp. 184–87.

Gerard, J. (1636) *Gerard's Herball,* T.H. Johnston (ed). Reduced version edited by Marcus Woodward (1927), reprinted by Bracken Books (1985).

Gill, R.C. (1941) *White Water and Black Magic,* London, Victor Gollancz.

Henfrey, C. (1964) *The Gentle People,* London, The Travel Book Club.

Lotschert, W. and Beese, G. (1981) *Collins Guide to Tropical Plants,* London, Collins.

Mayle, F.E., Burbridge, R. and Killeen, T.J. (2000) 'Millennial-scale dynamics of southern Amazonian rain forests' *Science,* vol. 290, no. 5500, pp. 2291–2294.

Nepstad, D.C., Stickler, C.M. and Almeida O.T. (2006) 'Globalization of the Amazon soy and beef industries: opportunities for conservation', *Conservation Biology,* vol. 6, pp. 1595–1603.

Nepstad, D.C., Stickler, C.M., Soares-Filho, B. and Merry, F. (2008) 'Interactions among Amazon land use, forests and climate: prospects for a near-term forest tipping point', *Philosophical Transactions of the Royal Society of London B,* vol. 363, pp. 1737–46.

Pearl, R. and Reed, L.J. (1920) 'On the rate of growth of the population in the United States since 1790 and its mathematical representation', *Proceedings of the National Academy of Sciences,* vol. 6, pp. 275–88.

Salisbury, D.S. and Schmink, M. (2007) 'Cows versus rubber: changing livelihoods among Amazonian extractivists', *Geoforum,* vol. 38, pp. 1233–49.

Schomburgk, R. (1840) *Richard Schomburgk's Travels in British Guiana, 1840–1844,* translated and edited by W.E. Roth, *Daily Chronicle,* Georgetown, British Guiana (1922–23).

Verweij, P., Schouten, M., Beukering, P., Triana, J., van der Leeuw, K. and Hess, S. (2009) *Keeping the Amazon Forests standing: a matter of values*, report commissioned by WWF Netherlands, http://assets.panda.org/downloads/wnf_amazonerapport_def.pdf (Accessed June 2009).

Waterton. C. (1889) *Wanderings in South America*, London, Macmillan (refers to journeys from 1812 to 1824).

WWF (2003) *Safeguarding the Amazon: The First Milestone – Tumucumaque*, World Wildlife Fund.

Acknowledgements

Grateful acknowledgement is made to the following sources:

Tables

Table 2.1: Whittaker, R.A. (1975) *Communities and ecosystems*, Macmillan London Limited; Tables 2.2 and 2.3: Achard et al. (2002) 'Determination and deforestation rates of the world's humid tropical forests', vol. 297, *Science*; Table 2.4: Clubbe, C. and Jhilmit, S. (2002) *Plant Conservation in the Tropics*, Royal Botanic Gardens, Kew; Table 3.1: Verweij, P. et al. (2009) *Keeping the Amazon Forests standing: a matter of values*, WWF Netherlands; Table 3.2 and Figure C: Verweij et al. (2009) *Keeping the Amazon Forests standing: a matter of values*, WWF, Netherlands; Table 3.4: Bisset, N.G (1992) 'War and hunting poisons of the New World Part 1', *Journal of Ethnopharmacology*, vol. 36, Elsevier; Table 3.6: Johnston T.H. (ed) (1984) *Gerard's Herball* (1626), Bracken Books.

Figures

Figure I.1a, 1.7 and 2.1: Taken from www.hydrosheds.cr.usgs.gov. Data produced by WWF; Figure 1.1b: © Bruce Farnsworth/Alamy; Figure 1.1d: Courtesy of Chris & Lina - "The Traveladdicts" at http://www.traveladdicts.connectfree.co.uk; Figure 1.3a: ©Amazon-Images/Alamy Images; Figure 1.3b: © Brian Cook/Alamy Images; Figure 1.3c: © Mark Harvey/Still Pictures; Figure 1.5: © Peter Arnold Inc./Alamy; Figure 1.8a & b: © Andrea Florence/Ardea Figure 1.8c: © Amazon-Images/Alamy; Figure 1.9: © Seapics.com; Figure 1.10a: Stevens, P.F. (2001 onwards) Angiosperm Phylogeny Website. Version 9, June 2008. www.mobot.org/MOBOT/research/Apweb/; Figure 1.10b: © Jacques Jangoux/Alamy; Figure 1.11: Courtesy of USDA Forest Service Southern Research Station; Figures 1.12, 1.14 & 1.16: © Michael Gillman; Figure 1.17b: © Cambridge University Library; Figures 1.18b & 1.19a: Courtesy of Hilary Erenler/Michael Gillman; Figures 1.15b, 1.15c, 1.19b & c, 1.21b, 1.22b, 1.23a, 1.13c, 1.23d, 1.26a, 1.27 & 1.29: © Michael Gillman; Figure 1.21a: Courtesy of The Virtual Fossil Museum www.fossilmuseum.net; Figure 1.22a: © blickwinkel/Alamy; Figure 1.23b: Taken from www.wikipedia.org and used under GNU Free Documentation Licence; Figure 1.24: Mountain High Maps ® Copyright © 1993 Digital Wisdom, Inc.; Figure 1.26b: © Bridgeman Art Library/Service Historique de la Marine Vincennes, France; Figure 2.5: Courtesy of Sassan Saatchi; Figure 2.8: North Atlantic Fisheries Organisation; Figure 2.9a: © Warren Kovach/Alamy; Figure 2.9b: © Mike Dodd; Figure 2.9c: © Warren Kovack/Alamy; Figure 2.10a: Taken from www.wikipedia.org and used under the GNU Free Documentation Licence; Figure 2.10b: Taken from www.wikipedia.org and used under Creative Commons; Figure 2.11a: © Mike Gillman; Figure 2.11b: © Worldwide Picture Library/Alamy; Figure 3.1: Courtesy of Sophia Braybrooke; Figure 3.2: Courtesy of the US Geological Survey; Figure 3.3a & b: Courtesy